THE
MAGICAL FOLK
OF IRELAND

THE
MAGICAL FOLK
OF IRELAND

THE
MAGICAL FOLK
OF IRELAND

W.B. YEATS

INSCRIBED

TO MY MYSTICAL FRIEND,

G. R.

Originally published as *Fairy and Folk Tales of the Irish Peasantry* in 1890

This edition published in 2024 by Arcturus Publishing Limited
26/27 Bickels Yard, 151–153 Bermondsey Street,
London SE1 3HA

Copyright © Arcturus Holdings Limited

All rights reserved. No part of this publication may be reproduced, stored in a retrieval system, or transmitted, in any form or by any means, electronic, mechanical, photocopying, recording or otherwise, without prior written permission in accordance with the provisions of the Copyright Act 1956 (as amended). Any person or persons who do any unauthorised act in relation to this publication may be liable to criminal prosecution and civil claims for damages.

AD012431UK

Printed in China

CONTENTS

INTRODUCTION 7

THE TROOPING FAIRIES 9

    FRANK MARTIN AND THE FAIRIES 12

    THE PRIEST'S SUPPER 16

    TEIG O'KANE AND THE CORPSE 20

    PADDY CORCORAN'S WIFE 34

    THE WHITE TROUT; A LEGEND OF CONG 36

    THE LEGEND OF KNOCKGRAFTON 39

    A DONEGAL FAIRY 44

CHANGELINGS 45

    THE BREWERY OF EGG-SHELLS 46

    JAMIE FREEL AND THE YOUNG LADY 49

    THE STOLEN CHILD 56

THE MERROW 58

    THE SOUL CAGES 59

    FLORY CANTILLON'S FUNERAL 72

THE SOLITARY FAIRIES 76

    LEPRACAUN. CLURICAUN. FAR DARRIG 76

    MASTER AND MAN 78

    FAR DARRIG IN DONEGAL 85

THE POOKA 88

    THE PIPER AND THE PUCA 89

    DANIEL O'ROURKE 92

    THE KILDARE POOKA 99

THE BANSHEE 102

    HOW THOMAS CONNOLLY MET THE BANSHEE 103

    THE BANSHEE OF THE MAC CARTHYS 106

GHOSTS 119

    A DREAM 121

    GRACE CONNOR 123

THE RADIANT BOY 125
THE FATE OF FRANK M'KENNA 128
WITCHES, FAIRY DOCTORS 134
BEWITCHED BUTTER (DONEGAL)................................. 138
A QUEEN'S COUNTY WITCH.. 140
THE WITCH HARE... 144
BEWITCHED BUTTER (QUEEN'S COUNTY)................. 145
THE WITCHES' EXCURSION 155
THE CONFESSIONS OF TOM BOURKE........................... 158
THE PUDDING BEWITCHED 172
T'YEER-NA-N-OGE... 185
THE LEGEND OF O'DONOGHUE 186
RENT-DAY 189
LOUGHLEAGH (LAKE OF HEALING) 192
THE PHANTOM ISLE 198
GIANTS 199
THE GIANT'S STAIRS 200
A LEGEND OF KNOCKMANY 206
KINGS, QUEENS, PRINCESSES, EARLS, ROBBERS 218
THE TWELVE WILD GEESE 218
THE LAZY BEAUTY AND HER AUNTS........................... 224
THE HAUGHTY PRINCESS 228
THE ENCHANTMENT OF GEAROIDH IARLA................ 231
MUNACHAR AND MANACHAR 234
DONALD AND HIS NEIGHBOURS................................. 238
THE JACKDAW 242
THE STORY OF CONN-EDA.. 245

INTRODUCTION

William Butler Yeats is considered to be one of the greatest poets of the 20th century. He was born in Dublin in 1865. His father, John Butler Yeats, was a well-known Irish painter, and his mother Susan Mary Pollexfen came from a family of merchants in Sligo.

When Yeats was two, the family moved to London where they remained for 14 years, before returning to Dublin in 1881. William studied at the Metropolitan School of Art and quickly discovered that he preferred poetry. His first collection of poems covering Ireland, its folklore, spiritualism and love was first published in 1889. Yeats later met and fell in love with Maud Gonne, an Irishwoman equally famous for her passionate nationalist politics and her beauty. She served as his muse for years, further inspiring his nationalism. Gonne is also said to have inspired his poetry by her rejection of his advances, and he persued her for the next three decades.

In 1890, Yeats helped set up the Rhymers' Club, a group of poets who met Ye Olde Cheshire Cheese pub in Fleet Street to recite and discuss their work. Committed also to playwriting, he penned *The Land of Heart's Desire* which was first performed in 1894 at the Avenue Theatre in London. Yeats was also a member of The Golden Dawn, a secret society that practised ritual magic.

In 1896, Yeats was introduced to the Irish dramatist Lady Gregory by their mutual friend Edward Martyn. He had written a number of successful 'nationalistic' plays in the early 1890s, and Gregory encouraged his nationalism and convinced him to focus on writing drama. This led to the founding of the Irish National Theatre Society – the society opened its doors in December 1904 and staged plays by Gregory and Yeats.

THE MAGICAL FOLK OF IRELAND

He continued to write poetry, and his style developed during the early years of the new century. Still retaining their traditional verse forms, symbolism and energy, Yeats' poems delved into the complexities of life, religion and politics. In 1917, he married Georgie Hyde-Lees – the couple had two children.

The political situation in Ireland in the post-war years was fraught with bitter controversy over the Irish Free State and the partition of Northern Ireland. Siding firmly with the Irish government, Yeats became involved politically and began serving as a senator in 1922. The following year, he was awarded the Nobel Prize in Literature 'for his always inspired poetry, which in a highly artistic form [gave] expression to the spirit of a whole nation.' The poems and plays that Yeats produced over the years that followed included his poem 'The Second Coming' and his first major poetry collection after winning the Nobel prize, *The Tower*. Published in 1928, it is often considered his best book.

This collection is an abridged version of *Fairy and Folk Tales of the Irish Peasantry* (1892), a volume of short stories and poems edited by Yeats. Included are some of Ireland's greatest writers such as Patrick Kennedy, Douglas Hyde, William Carleton, T. Crofton Croker and many more. Packed with adventure, magic and fantastical beings such as fairies, leprechauns and spirits, each tale in this carefully compiled volume shares the beliefs and customs of the Irish people and the culture that has long been crucial to their way of life.

As he approached the age of 60, Yeats' health began to fail and he was faced with 'bodily decrepitude'. Despite this, the last 15 years of his life were marked by extraordinary vitality and an appetite for life. He continued to write until his death in late January 1939.

THE TROOPING
FAIRIES

The Irish word for fairy is *sheehogue* [*sidheóg*], a diminutive of 'shee' in *banshee*. Fairies are *deenee shee* [*daoine sidhe*] (fairy people).

Who are they? 'Fallen angels who were not good enough to be saved, nor bad enough to be lost,' say the peasantry. 'The gods of the earth,' says the *Book of Armagh*. 'The gods of pagan Ireland,' say the Irish antiquarians, 'the *Tuatha De Danān*, who, when no longer worshipped and fed with offerings, dwindled away in the popular imagination, and now are only a few spans high.'

And they will tell you, in proof, that the names of fairy chiefs are the names of old *Danān* heroes, and the places where they especially gather together, *Danān* burying-places, and that the *Tuath De Danān* used also to be called the *slooa-shee* [*sheagh sidhe*] (the fairy host), or Marcra shee (the fairy cavalcade).

On the other hand, there is much evidence to prove them fallen angels. Witness the nature of the creatures, their caprice, their way of being good to the good and evil to the evil, having every charm but conscience – consistency. Beings so quickly offended that you must not speak much about them at all, and never call them anything but the 'gentry', or else *daoine maithe*, which in English means good people, yet so easily pleased, they will do their best to keep misfortune away from you, if you leave a little milk for them on the window-sill overnight. On the whole, the popular belief tells us most about them, telling us how they fell, and yet were not lost, because their evil was wholly without malice.

THE MAGICAL FOLK OF IRELAND

Are they 'the gods of the earth'? Perhaps! Many poets, and all mystic and occult writers, in all ages and countries, have declared that behind the visible are chains on chains of conscious beings, who are not of heaven but of the earth, who have no inherent form but change according to their whim, or the mind that sees them. You cannot lift your hand without influencing and being influenced by hordes. The visible world is merely their skin. In dreams we go amongst them, and play with them, and combat with them. They are, perhaps, human souls in the crucible – these creatures of whim.

Do not think the fairies are always little. Everything is capricious about them, even their size. They seem to take what size or shape pleases them. Their chief occupations are feasting, fighting, and making love, and playing the most beautiful music. They have only one industrious person amongst them, the *lepra-caun* – the shoemaker. Perhaps they wear their shoes out with dancing. Near the village of Ballisodare is a little woman who lived amongst them seven years. When she came home she had no toes – she had danced them off.

They have three great festivals in the year – May Eve, Midsummer Eve, November Eve. On May Eve, every seventh year, they fight all round, but mostly on the 'Plain-a-Bawn' (wherever that is), for the harvest, for the best ears of grain belong to them. An old man told me he saw them fight once; they tore the thatch off a house in the midst of it all. Had anyone else been near they would merely have seen a great wind whirling everything into the air as it passed. When the wind makes the straws and leaves whirl as it passes, that is the fairies, and the peasantry take off their hats and say, 'God bless them.'

On Midsummer Eve, when the bonfires are lighted on every hill in honour of St. John, the fairies are at their gayest, and sometime steal away beautiful mortals to be their brides.

On November Eve they are at their gloomiest, for, according to the old Gaelic reckoning, this is the first night of winter. This night they dance with the ghosts, and the pooka is abroad, and witches make their spells, and girls set a table with food in the name of the devil, that the fetch of their future lover may come through the window and eat of the

THE TROOPING FAIRIES

food. After November Eve the blackberries are no longer wholesome, for the *pooka* has spoiled them.

When they are angry, they paralyse men and cattle with their fairy darts.

When they are gay they sing. Many a poor girl has heard them, and pined away and died, for love of that singing. Plenty of the old beautiful tunes of Ireland are only their music, caught up by eavesdroppers. No wise peasant would hum 'The Pretty Girl milking the Cow' near a fairy rath, for they are jealous, and do not like to hear their songs on clumsy mortal lips. Carolan, the last of the Irish bards, slept on a rath, and ever after the fairy tunes ran in his head, and made him the great man he was.

Do they die? Blake saw a fairy's funeral; but in Ireland we say they are immortal.

FRANK MARTIN AND THE FAIRIES

William Carleton

Martin was a thin pale man, when I saw him, of a sickly look, and a constitution naturally feeble. His hair was a light auburn, his beard mostly unshaven, and his hands of a singular delicacy and whiteness, owing, I dare say, as much to the soft and easy nature of his employment as to his infirm health. In everything else he was as sensible, sober, and rational as any other man; but on the topic of fairies, the man's mania was peculiarly strong and immovable. Indeed, I remember that the expression of his eyes was singularly wild and hollow, and his long narrow temples sallow and emaciated.

Now, this man did not lead an unhappy life, nor did the malady he laboured under seem to be productive of either pain or terror to him, although one might be apt to imagine otherwise. On the contrary, he and the fairies maintained the most friendly intimacy, and their dialogues – which I fear were wofully one-sided ones – must have been a source of great pleasure to him, for they were conducted with much mirth and laughter, on his part at least.

'Well, Frank, when did you see the fairies?'

'Whist! There's two dozen of them in the shop (the weaving shop) this minute. There's a little ould fellow sittin' on the top of the sleys, an' all to be rocked while I'm weavin'. The sorrow's in them, but they're the greatest little skamers alive, so they are. See, there's another of them at my dressin' noggin.[1] Go out o' that, you *shingawn*; or, bad cess

---

1 The dressings are a species of sizy flummery, which is brushed into the yarn to keep the thread round and even, and to prevent it from being frayed by the friction of the reed.

FRANK MARTIN AND THE FAIRIES

to me, if you don't, but I'll lave you a mark. Ha! cut, you thief you!'

'Frank, arn't you afeard o' them?'

'Is it me! Arra, what 'ud I be afeard o' them for? Sure they have no power over me.'

'And why haven't they, Frank?'

'Because I was baptized against them.'

'What do you mean by that?'

'Why, the priest that christened me was tould by my father, to put in the proper prayer against the fairies – an' a priest can't refuse it when he's asked – an' he did so. Begorra, it's well for me that he did – (let the tallow alone, you little glutton – see, there's a weeny thief o' them aitin' my tallow) – becaise, you see, it was their intention to make me king o' the fairies.'

'Is it possible?'

'Devil a lie in it. Sure you may ax them, an' they'll tell you.'

'What size are they, Frank?'

'Oh, little wee fellows, with green coats, an' the purtiest little shoes ever you seen. There's two of them – both ould acquaintances o' mine – runnin' along the yarn-beam. That ould fellow with the bob-wig is called Jim Jam, an' the other chap, with the three-cocked hat, is called Nickey Nick. Nickey plays the pipes. Nickey, give us a tune, or I'll malivogue you – come now, "Lough Erne Shore". Whist, now – listen!'

The poor fellow, though weaving as fast as he could all the time, yet bestowed every possible mark of attention to the music, and seemed to enjoy it as much as if it had been real.

But who can tell whether that which we look upon as a privation may not after all be a fountain of increased happiness, greater, perhaps, than any which we ourselves enjoy? I forget who the poet is who says –

> 'Mysterious are thy laws;
> The vision's finer than the view;
> Her landscape Nature never drew
> So fair as Fancy draws.'

Many a time, when a mere child, not more than six or seven years

THE MAGICAL FOLK OF IRELAND

of age, have I gone as far as Frank's weaving-shop, in order, with a heart divided between curiosity and fear, to listen to his conversation with the good people. From morning till night his tongue was going almost as incessantly as his shuttle; and it was well known that at night, whenever he awoke out of his sleep, the first thing he did was to put out his hand, and push them, as it were, off his bed.

'Go out o' this, you thieves, you – go out o' this now, an' let me alone. Nickey, is this any time to be playing the pipes, and me wants to sleep? Go off, now – troth if yez do, you'll see what I'll give yez to-morrow. Sure I'll be makin' new dressin's; and if yez behave decently, maybe I'll lave yez the scrapin' o' the pot. There now. Och! pour things, they're dacent crathurs. Sure they're all gone, barrin' poor Red-cap, that doesn't like to lave me.' And then the harmless monomaniac would fall back into what we trust was an innocent slumber.

About this time there was said to have occurred a very remarkable circumstance, which gave poor Frank a vast deal of importance among the neighbours. A man named Frank Thomas, the same in whose house Mickey M'Rorey held the first dance at which I ever saw him, as detailed in a former sketch; this man, I say, had a child sick, but of what complaint I cannot now remember, nor is it of any importance. One of the gables of Thomas's house was built against, or rather into, a Forth or Rath, called Towny, or properly Tonagh Forth. It was said to be haunted by the fairies, and what gave it a character peculiarly wild in my eyes was, that there were on the southern side of it two or three little green mounds, which were said to be the graves of unchristened children, over which it was considered dangerous and unlucky to pass. At all events, the season was mid-summer; and one evening about dusk, during the illness of the child, the noise of a hand-saw was heard upon the Forth. This was considered rather strange, and, after a little time, a few of those who were assembled at Frank Thomas's went to see who it could be that was sawing in such a place, or what they could be sawing at so late an hour, for everyone knew that nobody in the whole country about them would dare to cut down the few white-thorns that grew upon the Forth. On going to examine, however, judge of their surprise, when, after surrounding and searching the whole

FRANK MARTIN AND THE FAIRIES

place, they could discover no trace of either saw or sawyer. In fact, with the exception of themselves, there was no one, either natural or supernatural, visible. They then returned to the house, and had scarcely sat down, when it was heard again within ten yards of them. Another examination of the premises took place, but with equal success. Now, however, while standing on the Forth, they heard the sawing in a little hollow, about a hundred and fifty yards below them, which was completely exposed to their view, but they could see nobody. A party of them immediately went down to ascertain, if possible, what this singular noise and invisible labour could mean; but on arriving at the spot, they heard the sawing, to which were now added hammering, and the driving of nails upon the Forth above, whilst those who stood on the Forth continued to hear it in the hollow. On comparing notes, they resolved to send down to Billy Nelson's for Frank Martin, a distance of only about eighty or ninety yards. He was soon on the spot, and without a moment's hesitation solved the enigma.

''Tis the fairies,' said he. 'I see them, and busy crathurs they are.'

'But what are they sawing, Frank?'

'They are makin' a child's coffin,' he replied; 'they have the body already made, an' they're now nailin' the lid together.'

That night the child died, and the story goes that on the second evening afterwards, the carpenter who was called upon to make the coffin brought a table out from Thomas's house to the Forth, as a temporary bench; and, it is said, that the sawing and hammering necessary for the completion of his task were precisely the same which had been heard the evening but one before – neither more nor less. I remember the death of the child myself, and the making of its coffin, but I think the story of the supernatural carpenter was not heard in the village for some months after its interment.

Frank had every appearance of a hypochondriac about him. At the time I saw him, he might be about thirty-four years of age, but I do not think, from the debility of his frame and infirm health, that he has been alive for several years. He was an object of considerable interest and curiosity, and often have I been present when he was pointed out to strangers as 'the man that could see the good people'.

THE PRIEST'S SUPPER

T. Crofton Croker

It is said by those who ought to understand such things, that the good people, or the fairies, are some of the angels who were turned out of heaven, and who landed on their feet in this world, while the rest of their companions, who had more sin to sink them, went down farther to a worse place. Be this as it may, there was a merry troop of the fairies, dancing and playing all manner of wild pranks, on a bright moonlight evening towards the end of September. The scene of their merriment was not far distant from Inchegeela, in the west of the county Cork – a poor village, although it had a barrack for soldiers; but great mountains and barren rocks, like those round about it, are enough to strike poverty into any place: however, as the fairies can have everything they want for wishing, poverty does not trouble them much, and all their care is to seek out unfrequented nooks and places where it is not likely any one will come to spoil their sport.

On a nice green sod by the river's side were the little fellows dancing in a ring as gaily as may be, with their red caps wagging about at every bound in the moonshine, and so light were these bounds that the lobs of dew, although they trembled under their feet, were not disturbed by their capering. Thus did they carry on their gambols, spinning round and round, and twirling and bobbing and diving, and going through all manner of figures, until one of them chirped out,

> 'Cease, cease, with your drumming,
> Here's an end to our mumming;
> By my smell
> I can tell
> A priest this way is coming!'

THE PRIEST'S SUPPER

And away every one of the fairies scampered off as hard as they could, concealing themselves under the green leaves of the lusmore, where, if their little red caps should happen to peep out, they would only look like its crimson bells; and more hid themselves at the shady side of stones and brambles, and others under the bank of the river, and in holes and crannies of one kind or another.

The fairy speaker was not mistaken; for along the road, which was within view of the river, came Father Horrigan on his pony, thinking to himself that as it was so late he would make an end of his journey at the first cabin he came to. According to this determination, he stopped at the dwelling of Dermod Leary, lifted the latch, and entered with 'My blessing on all here.'

I need not say that Father Horrigan was a welcome guest wherever he went, for no man was more pious or better beloved in the country. Now it was a great trouble to Dermod that he had nothing to offer his reverence for supper as a relish to the potatoes, which 'the old woman', for so Dermod called his wife, though she was not much past twenty, had down boiling in a pot over the fire; he thought of the net which he had set in the river, but as it had been there only a short time, the chances were against his finding a fish in it. 'No matter,' thought Dermod, 'there can be no harm in stepping down to try; and maybe, as I want the fish for the priest's supper, that one will be there before me.'

Down to the river-side went Dermod, and he found in the net as fine a salmon as ever jumped in the bright waters of 'the spreading Lee'; but as he was going to take it out, the net was pulled from him, he could not tell how or by whom, and away got the salmon, and went swimming along with the current as gaily as if nothing had happened.

Dermod looked sorrowfully at the wake which the fish had left upon the water, shining like a line of silver in the moonlight, and then, with an angry motion of his right hand, and a stamp of his foot, gave vent to his feelings by muttering, 'May bitter bad luck attend you night and day for a blackguard schemer of a salmon, wherever you go! You ought to be ashamed of yourself, if there's any shame in you, to give me the slip after this fashion! And I'm clear in my own mind you'll come to no good, for some kind of evil thing or other helped you – did I not feel it

THE MAGICAL FOLK OF IRELAND

pull the net against me as strong as the devil himself?'

'That's not true for you,' said one of the little fairies who had scampered off at the approach of the priest, coming up to Dermod Leary with a whole throng of companions at his heels; 'there was only a dozen and a half of us pulling against you.'

Dermod gazed on the tiny speaker with wonder, who continued, 'Make yourself noways uneasy about the priest's supper; for if you will go back and ask him one question from us, there will be as fine a supper as ever was put on a table spread out before him in less than no time.'

'I'll have nothing at all to do with you,' replied Dermod in a tone of determination; and after a pause he added, 'I'm much obliged to you for your offer, sir, but I know better than to sell myself to you, or the like of you, for a supper; and more than that, I know Father Horrigan has more regard for my soul than to wish me to pledge it for ever, out of regard to anything you could put before him – so there's an end of the matter.'

The little speaker, with a pertinacity not to be repulsed by Dermod's manner, continued, 'Will you ask the priest one civil question for us?'

Dermod considered for some time, and he was right in doing so, but he thought that no one could come to harm out of asking a civil question. 'I see no objection to do that same, gentlemen,' said Dermod; 'but I will have nothing in life to do with your supper – mind that.'

'Then,' said the little speaking fairy, whilst the rest came crowding after him from all parts, 'go and ask Father Horrigan to tell us whether our souls will be saved at the last day, like the souls of good Christians; and if you wish us well, bring back word what he says without delay.'

Away went Dermod to his cabin, where he found the potatoes thrown out on the table, and his good woman handing the biggest of them all, a beautiful laughing red apple, smoking like a hard-ridden horse on a frosty night, over to Father Horrigan.

'Please your reverence,' said Dermod, after some hesitation, 'may I make bold to ask your honour one question?'

'What may that be?' said Father Horrigan.

'Why, then, begging your reverence's pardon for my freedom, it is,

THE PRIEST'S SUPPER

If the souls of the good people are to be saved at the last day?'

'Who bid you ask me that question, Leary?' said the priest, fixing his eyes upon him very sternly, which Dermod could not stand before at all.

'I'll tell no lies about the matter, and nothing in life but the truth,' said Dermod. 'It was the good people themselves who sent me to ask the question, and there they are in thousands down on the bank of the river, waiting for me to go back with the answer.'

'Go back by all means,' said the priest, 'and tell them, if they want to know, to come here to me themselves, and I'll answer that or any other question they are pleased to ask with the greatest pleasure in life.'

Dermod accordingly returned to the fairies, who came swarming round about him to hear what the priest had said in reply; and Dermod spoke out among them like a bold man as he was: but when they heard that they must go to the priest, away they fled, some here and more there, and some this way and more that, whisking by poor Dermod so fast and in such numbers that he was quite bewildered.

When he came to himself, which was not for a long time, back he went to his cabin, and ate his dry potatoes along with Father Horrigan, who made quite light of the thing; but Dermod could not help thinking it a mighty hard case that his reverence, whose words had the power to banish the fairies at such a rate, should have no sort of relish to his supper, and that the fine salmon he had in the net should have been got away from him in such a manner.

TEIG O'KANE (TADHG O CÁTHÁN) AND THE CORPSE[1]

Literally translated from the Irish by Douglas Hyde

[I found it hard to place Mr Douglas Hyde's magnificent story. Among the ghosts or the fairies? It is among the fairies on the grounds that all these ghosts and bodies were in no manner ghosts and bodies, but *pishogues* – fairy spells. One often hears of these visions in Ireland. I have met a man who had lived a wild life like the man in the story, till a vision came to him in County — one dark night – in no way so terrible a vision as this, but sufficient to change his whole character. He will not go out at night. If you speak to him suddenly, he trembles. He has grown timid and strange. He went to the bishop and was sprinkled with holy water. 'It may have come as a warning,' said the bishop; 'yet great theologians are of opinion that no man ever saw an apparition, for no man would survive it.' – Ed.]

There was once a grown-up lad in the County Leitrim, and he was strong and lively, and the son of a rich farmer. His father had plenty of money, and he did not spare it on the son. Accordingly, when the boy grew up he liked sport better than work, and, as his father had no other children, he loved this one so much that he allowed him to do in everything just as it pleased himself. He was very extravagant, and he used to scatter the gold money as another person would scatter the white. He was seldom to be found at home, but if there was a fair, or a

---

1 None of Mr Hyde's stories here given have been published before. They will be printed in the original Irish in his forthcoming *Leabhar Sgeulaigheachta* (Gill, Dublin).

TEIG O'KANE AND THE CORPSE

race, or a gathering within ten miles of him, you were dead certain to find him there. And he seldom spent a night in his father's house, but he used to be always out rambling, and, like Shawn Bwee long ago, there was

'grádh gach cailín i mbrollach a léine,'

'the love of every girl in the breast of his shirt,' and it's many's the kiss he got and he gave, for he was very handsome, and there wasn't a girl in the country but would fall in love with him, only for him to fasten his two eyes on her, and it was for that someone made this rann on him –

'Feuch an rógaire 'g iarraidh póige,
Ni h-iongantas mór é a bheith mar atá
Ag leanamhaint a gcómhnuidhe d'arnan na gráineóige
Anuas 's anios 's nna chodladh 'sa' lá.'

i.e. – 'Look at the rogue, it's for kisses he's rambling,
It isn't much wonder, for that was his way;
He's like an old hedgehog, at night he'll be scrambling
From this place to that, but he'll sleep in the day.'

At last he became very wild and unruly. He wasn't to be seen day nor night in his father's house, but always rambling or going on his *kailee* (night-visit) from place to place and from house to house, so that the old people used to shake their heads and say to one another, 'It's easy seen what will happen to the land when the old man dies; his son will run through it in a year, and it won't stand him that long itself.'

He used to be always gambling and card-playing and drinking, but his father never minded his bad habits, and never punished him. But it happened one day that the old man was told that the son had ruined the character of a girl in the neighbourhood, and he was greatly angry, and he called the son to him, and said to him, quietly and sensibly – *'Avic,'*

THE MAGICAL FOLK OF IRELAND

says he, 'you know I loved you greatly up to this, and I never stopped you from doing your choice thing whatever it was, and I kept plenty of money with you, and I always hoped to leave you the house and land, and all I had after myself would be gone; but I heard a story of you to-day that has disgusted me with you. I cannot tell you the grief that I felt when I heard such a thing of you, and I tell you now plainly that unless you marry that girl I'll leave house and land and everything to my brother's son. I never could leave it to anyone who would make so bad a use of it as you do yourself, deceiving women and coaxing girls. Settle with yourself now whether you'll marry that girl and get my land as a fortune with her, or refuse to marry her and give up all that was coming to you; and tell me in the morning which of the two things you have chosen.'

'Och! *Domnoo Sheery*! father, you wouldn't say that to me, and I such a good son as I am. Who told you I wouldn't marry the girl?' says he.

But his father was gone, and the lad knew well enough that he would keep his word too; and he was greatly troubled in his mind, for as quiet and as kind as the father was, he never went back of a word that he had once said, and there wasn't another man in the country who was harder to bend than he was.

The boy did not know rightly what to do. He was in love with the girl indeed, and he hoped to marry her sometime or other, but he would much sooner have remained another while as he was, and follow on at his old tricks – drinking, sporting, and playing cards; and, along with that, he was angry that his father should order him to marry, and should threaten him if he did not do it.

'Isn't my father a great fool,' says he to himself. 'I was ready enough, and only too anxious, to marry Mary; and now since he threatened me, faith I've a great mind to let it go another while.'

His mind was so much excited that he remained between two notions as to what he should do. He walked out into the night at last to cool his heated blood, and went on to the road. He lit a pipe, and as the night was fine he walked and walked on, until the quick pace made him begin to forget his trouble. The night was bright, and the moon half full.

TEIG O'KANE AND THE CORPSE

There was not a breath of wind blowing, and the air was calm and mild. He walked on for nearly three hours, when he suddenly remembered that it was late in the night, and time for him to turn. '*Musha*! I think I forgot myself,' says he; 'it must be near twelve o'clock now.'

The word was hardly out of his mouth, when he heard the sound of many voices, and the trampling of feet on the road before him. 'I don't know who can be out so late at night as this, and on such a lonely road,' said he to himself.

He stood listening, and he heard the voices of many people talking through other, but he could not understand what they were saying. 'Oh, *wirra*!' says he, 'I'm afraid. It's not Irish or English they have; it can't be they're Frenchmen!' He went on a couple of yards further, and he saw well enough by the light of the moon a band of little people coming towards him, and they were carrying something big and heavy with them. 'Oh, murder!' says he to himself, 'sure it can't be that they're the good people that's in it!' Every *rib* of hair that was on his head stood up, and there fell a shaking on his bones, for he saw that they were coming to him fast.

He looked at them again, and perceived that there were about twenty little men in it, and there was not a man at all of them higher than about three feet or three feet and a half, and some of them were grey, and seemed very old. He looked again, but he could not make out what was the heavy thing they were carrying until they came up to him, and then they all stood round about him. They threw the heavy thing down on the road, and he saw on the spot that it was a dead body.

He became as cold as the Death, and there was not a drop of blood running in his veins when an old little grey *maneen* came up to him and said, 'Isn't it lucky we met you, Teig O'Kane?'

Poor Teig could not bring out a word at all, nor open his lips, if he were to get the world for it, and so he gave no answer.

'Teig O'Kane,' said the little grey man again, 'isn't it timely you met us?'

Teig could not answer him.

'Teig O'Kane,' says he, the third time, 'isn't it lucky and timely that we met you?'

THE MAGICAL FOLK OF IRELAND

But Teig remained silent, for he was afraid to return an answer, and his tongue was as if it was tied to the roof of his mouth.

The little grey man turned to his companions, and there was joy in his bright little eye. 'And now,' says he, 'Teig O'Kane hasn't a word, we can do with him what we please. Teig, Teig,' says he, 'you're living a bad life, and we can make a slave of you now, and you cannot withstand us, for there's no use in trying to go against us. Lift that corpse.'

Teig was so frightened that he was only able to utter the two words, 'I won't'; for as frightened as he was, he was obstinate and stiff, the same as ever.

'Teig O'Kane won't lift the corpse,' said the little *maneen*, with a wicked little laugh, for all the world like the breaking of a *lock* of dry *kippeens*, and with a little harsh voice like the striking of a cracked bell. 'Teig O'Kane won't lift the corpse – make him lift it'; and before the word was out of his mouth they had all gathered round poor Teig, and they all talking and laughing through other.

Teig tried to run from them, but they followed him, and a man of them stretched out his foot before him as he ran, so that Teig was thrown in a heap on the road. Then before he could rise up the fairies caught him, some by the hands and some by the feet, and they held him tight, in a way that he could not stir, with his face against the ground. Six or seven of them raised the body then, and pulled it over to him, and left it down on his back. The breast of the corpse was squeezed against Teig's back and shoulders, and the arms of the corpse were thrown around Teig's neck. Then they stood back from him a couple of yards, and let him get up. He rose, foaming at the mouth and cursing, and he shook himself, thinking to throw the corpse off his back. But his fear and his wonder were great when he found that the two arms had a tight hold round his own neck, and that the two legs were squeezing his hips firmly, and that, however strongly he tried, he could not throw it off, any more than a horse can throw off its saddle. He was terribly frightened then, and he thought he was lost. 'Ochone! for ever,' said he to himself, 'it's the bad life I'm leading that has given the good people this power over me. I promise to God and Mary, Peter and Paul, Patrick and Bridget, that I'll mend my ways for as long as I

TEIG O'KANE AND THE CORPSE

have to live, if I come clear out of this danger – and I'll marry the girl.'

The little grey man came up to him again, and said he to him, 'Now, *Teigeen*,' says he, 'you didn't lift the body when I told you to lift it, and see how you were made to lift it; perhaps when I tell you to bury it you won't bury it until you're made to bury it!'

'Anything at all that I can do for your honour,' said Teig, 'I'll do it,' for he was getting sense already, and if it had not been for the great fear that was on him, he never would have let that civil word slip out of his mouth.

The little man laughed a sort of laugh again. 'You're getting quiet now, Teig,' says he. 'I'll go bail but you'll be quiet enough before I'm done with you. Listen to me now, Teig O'Kane, and if you don't obey me in all I'm telling you to do, you'll repent it. You must carry with you this corpse that is on your back to Teampoll-Démus, and you must bring it into the church with you, and make a grave for it in the very middle of the church, and you must raise up the flags and put them down again the very same way, and you must carry the clay out of the church and leave the place as it was when you came, so that no one could know that there had been anything changed. But that's not all. Maybe that the body won't be allowed to be buried in that church; perhaps some other man has the bed, and, if so, it's likely he won't share it with this one. If you don't get leave to bury it in Teampoll-Démus, you must carry it to Carrick-fhad-vic-Orus, and bury it in the churchyard there; and if you don't get it into that place, take it with you to Teampoll-Ronan; and if that churchyard is closed on you, take it to Imlogue-Fada; and if you're not able to bury it there, you've no more to do than to take it to Kill-Breedya, and you can bury it there without hindrance. I cannot tell you what one of those churches is the one where you will have leave to bury that corpse under the clay, but I know that it will be allowed you to bury him at some church or other of them. If you do this work rightly, we will be thankful to you, and you will have no cause to grieve; but if you are slow or lazy, believe me we shall take satisfaction of you.'

When the grey little man had done speaking, his comrades laughed and clapped their hands together. 'Glic! Glic! Hwee! Hwee!' they all

25

THE MAGICAL FOLK OF IRELAND

cried; 'go on, go on, you have eight hours before you till daybreak, and if you haven't this man buried before the sun rises, you're lost.' They struck a fist and a foot behind on him, and drove him on in the road. He was obliged to walk, and to walk fast, for they gave him no rest.

He thought himself that there was not a wet path, or a dirty boreen, or a crooked contrary road in the whole county, that he had not walked that night. The night was at times very dark, and whenever there would come a cloud across the moon he could see nothing, and then he used often to fall. Sometimes he was hurt, and sometimes he escaped, but he was obliged always to rise on the moment and to hurry on. Sometimes the moon would break out clearly, and then he would look behind him and see the little people following at his back. And he heard them speaking amongst themselves, talking and crying out, and screaming like a flock of sea-gulls; and if he was to save his soul he never understood as much as one word of what they were saying.

He did not know how far he had walked, when at last one of them cried out to him, 'Stop here!' He stood, and they all gathered round him.

'Do you see those withered trees over there?' says the old boy to him again. 'Teampoll-Démus is among those trees, and you must go in there by yourself, for we cannot follow you or go with you. We must remain here. Go on boldly.'

Teig looked from him, and he saw a high wall that was in places half broken down, and an old grey church on the inside of the wall, and about a dozen withered old trees scattered here and there round it. There was neither leaf nor twig on any of them, but their bare crooked branches were stretched out like the arms of an angry man when he threatens. He had no help for it, but was obliged to go forward. He was a couple of hundred yards from the church, but he walked on, and never looked behind him until he came to the gate of the churchyard. The old gate was thrown down, and he had no difficulty in entering. He turned then to see if any of the little people were following him, but there came a cloud over the moon, and the night became so dark that he could see nothing. He went into the churchyard, and he walked up the old grassy pathway leading to the church. When he reached the door, he found it locked. The door was large and strong, and he did not know

TEIG O'KANE AND THE CORPSE

what to do. At last he drew out his knife with difficulty, and stuck it in the wood to try if it were not rotten, but it was not.

'Now,' said he to himself, 'I have no more to do; the door is shut, and I can't open it.'

Before the words were rightly shaped in his own mind, a voice in his ear said to him, 'Search for the key on the top of the door, or on the wall.'

He started. 'Who is that speaking to me?' he cried, turning round; but he saw no one. The voice said in his ear again, 'Search for the key on the top of the door, or on the wall.'

'What's that?' said he, and the sweat running from his forehead; 'who spoke to me?'

'It's I, the corpse, that spoke to you!' said the voice.

'Can you talk?' said Teig.

'Now and again,' said the corpse.

Teig searched for the key, and he found it on the top of the wall. He was too much frightened to say any more, but he opened the door wide, and as quickly as he could, and he went in, with the corpse on his back. It was as dark as pitch inside, and poor Teig began to shake and tremble.

'Light the candle,' said the corpse.

Teig put his hand in his pocket, as well as he was able, and drew out a flint and steel. He struck a spark out of it, and lit a burnt rag he had in his pocket. He blew it until it made a flame, and he looked round him. The church was very ancient, and part of the wall was broken down. The windows were blown in or cracked, and the timber of the seats was rotten. There were six or seven old iron candlesticks left there still, and in one of these candlesticks Teig found the stump of an old candle, and he lit it. He was still looking round him on the strange and horrid place in which he found himself, when the cold corpse whispered in his ear, 'Bury me now, bury me now; there is a spade and turn the ground.' Teig looked from him, and he saw a spade lying beside the altar. He took it up, and he placed the blade under a flag that was in the middle of the aisle, and leaning all his weight on the handle of the spade, he raised it. When the first flag was raised it was not hard to

THE MAGICAL FOLK OF IRELAND

raise the others near it, and he moved three or four of them out of their places. The clay that was under them was soft and easy to dig, but he had not thrown up more than three or four shovelfuls, when he felt the iron touch something soft like flesh. He threw up three or four more shovelfuls from around it, and then he saw that it was another body that was buried in the same place.

'I am afraid I'll never be allowed to bury the two bodies in the same hole,' said Teig, in his own mind. 'You corpse, there on my back,' says he, 'will you be satisfied if I bury you down here?' But the corpse never answered him a word.

'That's a good sign,' said Teig to himself. 'Maybe he's getting quiet,' and he thrust the spade down in the earth again. Perhaps he hurt the flesh of the other body, for the dead man that was buried there stood up in the grave, and shouted an awful shout. 'Hoo! hoo!! hoo!!! Go! Go!! go!!! or you're a dead, dead, dead man!' And then he fell back in the grave again. Teig said afterwards, that of all the wonderful things he saw that night, that was the most awful to him. His hair stood upright on his head like the bristles of a pig, the cold sweat ran off his face, and then came a tremor over all his bones, until he thought that he must fall.

But after a while he became bolder, when he saw that the second corpse remained lying quietly there, and he threw in the clay on it again, and he smoothed it overhead and he laid down the flags carefully as they had been before. 'It can't be that he'll rise up any more,' said he.

He went down the aisle a little further, and drew near to the door, and began raising the flags again, looking for another bed for the corpse on his back. He took up three or four flags and put them aside, and then he dug the clay. He was not long digging until he laid bare an old woman without a thread upon her but her shirt. She was more lively than the first corpse, for he had scarcely taken any of the clay away from about her, when she sat up and began to cry, 'Ho, you *bodach* (clown)! Ha, you *bodach*! Where has he been that he got no bed?'

Poor Teig drew back, and when she found that she was getting no answer, she closed her eyes gently, lost her vigour, and fell back quietly and slowly under the clay. Teig did to her as he had done to the man – he threw the clay back on her, and left the flags down overhead.

28

TEIG O'KANE AND THE CORPSE

He began digging again near the door, but before he had thrown up more than a couple of shovelfuls, he noticed a man's hand laid bare by the spade. 'By my soul, I'll go no further, then,' said he to himself; 'what use is it for me?' And he threw the clay in again on it, and settled the flags as they had been before.

He left the church then, and his heart was heavy enough, but he shut the door and locked it, and left the key where he found it. He sat down on a tombstone that was near the door, and began thinking. He was in great doubt what he should do. He laid his face between his two hands, and cried for grief and fatigue, since he was dead certain at this time that he never would come home alive. He made another attempt to loosen the hands of the corpse that were squeezed round his neck, but they were as tight as if they were clamped; and the more he tried to loosen them, the tighter they squeezed him. He was going to sit down once more, when the cold, horrid lips of the dead man said to him, 'Carrick-fhad-vic-Orus', and he remembered the command of the good people to bring the corpse with him to that place if he should be unable to bury it where he had been.

He rose up, and looked about him. 'I don't know the way,' he said.

As soon as he had uttered the word, the corpse stretched out suddenly its left hand that had been tightened round his neck, and kept it pointing out, showing him the road he ought to follow. Teig went in the direction that the fingers were stretched, and passed out of the churchyard. He found himself on an old rutty, stony road, and he stood still again, not knowing where to turn. The corpse stretched out its bony hand a second time, and pointed out to him another road – not the road by which he had come when approaching the old church. Teig followed that road, and whenever he came to a path or road meeting it, the corpse always stretched out its hand and pointed with its fingers, showing him the way he was to take.

Many was the cross-road he turned down, and many was the crooked *boreen* he walked, until he saw from him an old burying-ground at last, beside the road, but there was neither church nor chapel nor any other building in it. The corpse squeezed him tightly, and he stood. 'Bury me, bury me in the burying-ground,' said the voice.

THE MAGICAL FOLK OF IRELAND

Teig drew over towards the old burying-place, and he was not more than about twenty yards from it, when, raising his eyes, he saw hundreds and hundreds of ghosts – men, women, and children – sitting on the top of the wall round about, or standing on the inside of it, or running backwards and forwards, and pointing at him, while he could see their mouths opening and shutting as if they were speaking, though he heard no word, nor any sound amongst them at all.

He was afraid to go forward, so he stood where he was, and the moment he stood, all the ghosts became quiet, and ceased moving. Then Teig understood that it was trying to keep him from going in, that they were. He walked a couple of yards forwards, and immediately the whole crowd rushed together towards the spot to which he was moving, and they stood so thickly together that it seemed to him that he never could break through them, even though he had a mind to try. But he had no mind to try it. He went back broken and dispirited, and when he had gone a couple of hundred yards from the burying-ground, he stood again, for he did not know what way he was to go. He heard the voice of the corpse in his ear, saying 'Teampoll-Ronan', and the skinny hand was stretched out again, pointing him out the road.

As tired as he was, he had to walk, and the road was neither short nor even. The night was darker than ever, and it was difficult to make his way. Many was the toss he got, and many a bruise they left on his body. At last he saw Teampoll-Ronan from him in the distance, standing in the middle of the burying-ground. He moved over towards it, and thought he was all right and safe, when he saw no ghosts nor anything else on the wall, and he thought he would never be hindered now from leaving his load off him at last. He moved over to the gate, but as he was passing in, he tripped on the threshold. Before he could recover himself, something that he could not see seized him by the neck, by the hands, and by the feet, and bruised him, and shook him, and choked him, until he was nearly dead; and at last he was lifted up, and carried more than a hundred yards from that place, and then thrown down in an old dyke, with the corpse still clinging to him.

He rose up, bruised and sore, but feared to go near the place again, for he had seen nothing the time he was thrown down and carried away.

TEIG O'KANE AND THE CORPSE

'You corpse, up on my back,' said he, 'shall I go over again to the churchyard?' – but the corpse never answered him. 'That's a sign you don't wish me to try it again,' said Teig.

He was now in great doubt as to what he ought to do, when the corpse spoke in his ear, and said 'Imlogue-Fada.'

'Oh, murder!' said Teig, 'must I bring you there? If you keep me long walking like this, I tell you I'll fall under you.'

He went on, however, in the direction the corpse pointed out to him. He could not have told, himself, how long he had been going, when the dead man behind suddenly squeezed him, and said, 'There!'

Teig looked from him, and he saw a little low wall, that was so broken down in places that it was no wall at all. It was in a great wide field, in from the road; and only for three or four great stones at the corners, that were more like rocks than stones, there was nothing to show that there was either graveyard or burying-ground there.

'Is this Imlogue-Fada? Shall I bury you here?' said Teig.

'Yes,' said the voice.

'But I see no grave or gravestone, only this pile of stones,' said Teig.

The corpse did not answer, but stretched out its long fleshless hand, to show Teig the direction in which he was to go. Teig went on accordingly, but he was greatly terrified, for he remembered what had happened to him at the last place. He went on, 'with his heart in his mouth', as he said himself afterwards; but when he came to within fifteen or twenty yards of the little low square wall, there broke out a flash of lightning, bright yellow and red, with blue streaks in it, and went round about the wall in one course, and it swept by as fast as the swallow in the clouds, and the longer Teig remained looking at it the faster it went, till at last it became like a bright ring of flame round the old graveyard, which no one could pass without being burnt by it. Teig never saw, from the time he was born, and never saw afterwards, so wonderful or so splendid a sight as that was. Round went the flame, white and yellow and blue sparks leaping out from it as it went, and although at first it had been no more than a thin, narrow line, it increased slowly until it was at last a great broad band, and it was continually getting broader and higher, and throwing out more brilliant sparks, till there was never a colour on the ridge of the earth that was not to be seen in that fire; and lightning never shone and flame never flamed that was so shining and so bright as that.

Teig was amazed; he was half dead with fatigue, and he had no courage left to approach the wall. There fell a mist over his eyes, and there came a soorawn in his head, and he was obliged to sit down upon a great stone to recover himself. He could see nothing but the light, and he could hear nothing but the whirr of it as it shot round the paddock faster than a flash of lightning.

As he sat there on the stone, the voice whispered once more in his ear, 'Kill-Breedya'; and the dead man squeezed him so tightly that he cried out. He rose again, sick, tired and trembling, and went forwards as he was directed. The wind was cold, and the road was bad, and the load upon his back was heavy, and the night was dark, and he himself was nearly worn out, and if he had had very much farther to go he must have fallen dead under his burden.

At last the corpse stretched out its hand, and said to him, 'Bury me there.'

'This is the last burying-place,' said Teig in his own mind; 'and the little grey man said I'd be allowed to bury him in some of them, so it must be this; it can't be but they'll let him in here.'

The first faint streak of the *ring of day* was appearing in the east, and the clouds were beginning to catch fire, but it was darker than ever, for the moon was set, and there were no stars.

'Make haste, make haste!' said the corpse; and Teig hurried forward as well as he could to the graveyard, which was a little place on a bare hill, with only a few graves in it. He walked boldly in through the open gate, and nothing touched him, nor did he either hear or see anything. He came to the middle of the ground, and then stood up and looked round him for a spade or shovel to make a grave. As he was turning round and searching, he suddenly perceived what startled him greatly – a newly dug grave right before him. He moved over to it, and looked down, and there at the bottom he saw a black coffin. He clambered down into the hole and lifted the lid, and found that (as he thought it

TEIG O'KANE AND THE CORPSE

would be) the coffin was empty. He had hardly mounted up out of the hole, and was standing on the brink, when the corpse, which had clung to him for more than eight hours, suddenly relaxed its hold of his neck, and loosened its shins from round his hips, and sank down with a *plop* into the open coffin.

Teig fell down on his two knees at the brink of the grave, and gave thanks to God. He made no delay then, but pressed down the coffin lid in its place, and threw in the clay over it with his two hands; and when the grave was filled up, he stamped and leaped on it with his feet, until it was firm and hard, and then he left the place.

The sun was fast rising as he finished his work, and the first thing he did was to return to the road, and look out for a house to rest himself in. He found an inn at last, and lay down upon a bed there, and slept till night. Then he rose up and ate a little, and fell asleep again till morning.

When he awoke in the morning he hired a horse and rode home. He was more than twenty-six miles from home where he was, and he had come all that way with the dead body on his back in one night.

All the people at his own home thought that he must have left the country, and they rejoiced greatly when they saw him come back. Everyone began asking him where he had been, but he would not tell anyone except his father.

He was a changed man from that day. He never drank too much; he never lost his money over cards; and especially he would not take the world and be out late by himself of a dark night.

He was not a fortnight at home until he married Mary, the girl he had been in love with; and it's at their wedding the sport was, and it's he was the happy man from that day forward, and it's all I wish that we may be as happy as he was.

Glossary: *Rann*, a stanza; *kailee* (*céilidhe*), a visit in the evening; *wirra* (a *mhuire*), 'Oh, Mary!' an exclamation like the French *dame*; *rib*, a single hair (in Irish, *ribe*); a *lock* (*glac*), a bundle or wisp, or a little share of anything; *kippeen* (*cipín*), a rod or twig; *boreen* (*bóithrin*), a lane; *bodach*, a clown; *soorawn* (*suarán*). vertigo. *Avic* (a *Mhic*) = my son, or rather, Oh, son. Mic is the vocative of Mac.

PADDY CORCORAN'S WIFE

William Carleton

Paddy Corcoran's wife was for several years afflicted with a kind of complaint which nobody could properly understand. She was sick, and she was not sick; she was well, and she was not well; she was as ladies wish to be who love their lords, and she was not as such ladies wish to be. In fact nobody could tell what the matter with her was. She had a gnawing at the heart which came heavily upon her husband; for, with the help of God, a keener appetite than the same gnawing amounted to could not be met with of a summer's day. The poor woman was delicate beyond belief, and had no appetite at all, so she hadn't, barring a little relish for a mutton-chop, or a 'staik', or a bit o' mait, anyway; for sure, God help her! she hadn't the laist inclination for the dhry pratie, or the dhrop o' sour buttermilk along wid it, especially as she was so poorly; and, indeed, for a woman in her condition – for, sick as she was, poor Paddy always was made to believe her in *that* condition – but God's will be done! she didn't care. A pratie an' a grain o' salt was a welcome to her – glory be to his name! – as the best roast an' boiled that ever was dressed; and why not? There was one comfort: she wouldn't be long wid him – long troublin' him; it matthered little what she got; but sure she knew herself, that from the gnawin' at her heart, she could never do good widout the little bit o' mait now and then; an', sure, if her own husband begridged it to her, who else had she a better right to expect it from?

Well, as we have said, she lay a bedridden invalid for long enough, trying doctors and quacks of all sorts, sexes and sizes, and all without a farthing's benefit, until, at the long run, poor Paddy was nearly brought to the last pass, in striving to keep her in 'the bit o' mait'. The seventh year was now on the point of closing, when, one harvest day, as she lay

PADDY CORCORAN'S WIFE

bemoaning her hard condition, on her bed beyond the kitchen fire, a little weeshy woman, dressed in a neat red cloak, comes in, and, sitting down by the hearth, says: –

'Well, Kitty Corcoran, you've had a long lair of it there on the broad o' yer back for seven years, an' you're jist as far from bein' cured as ever.'

'Mavrone, ay,' said the other; 'in throth that's what I was this minnit thinkin' ov, and a sorrowful thought it's to me.'

'It's yer own fau't, thin,' says the little woman; 'an', indeed, for that matter, it's yer fau't that ever you wor there at all.'

'Arra, how is that?' asked Kitty; 'sure I wouldn't be here if I could help it? Do you think it's a comfort or a pleasure to me to be sick and bedridden?'

'No,' said the other, 'I do not; but I'll tell you the truth: for the last seven years you have been annoying us. I am one o' the good people; an' as I have a regard for you, I'm come to let you know the raison why you've been sick so long as you are. For all the time you've been ill, if you'll take the thrubble to remimber, your childhre threwn out yer dirty wather afther dusk an' before sunrise, at the very time we're passin' yer door, which we pass twice a-day. Now, if you avoid this, if you throw it out in a different place, an' at a different time, the complaint you have will lave you: so will the gnawin' at the heart; an' you'll be as well as ever you wor. If you don't follow this advice, why, remain as you are, an' all the art o' man can't cure you.' She then bade her good-bye, and disappeared.

Kitty, who was glad to be cured on such easy terms, immediately complied with the injunction of the fairy; and the consequence was, that the next day she found herself in as good health as ever she enjoyed during her life.

THE WHITE TROUT;
A LEGEND OF CONG

By S. Lover

There was wanst upon a time, long ago, a beautiful lady that lived in a castle upon the lake beyant, and they say she was promised to a king's son, and they wor to be married, when all of a sudden he was murthered, the crathur (Lord help us), and threwn into the lake above, and so, of course, he couldn't keep his promise to the fair lady, – and more's the pity.

Well, the story goes that she went out iv her mind, bekase av loosin' the king's son – for she was tendher-hearted, God help her, like the rest iv us! – and pined away after him, until at last, no one about seen her, good or bad; and the story wint that the fairies took her away.

Well, sir, in coorse o' time, the White Throut, God bless it, was seen in the sthrame beyant, and sure the people didn't know what to think av the crathur, seein' as how a white throut was never heard av afor, nor since; and years upon years the throut was there, just where you seen it this blessed minit, longer nor I can tell – aye throth, and beyant the memory o' th' ouldest in the village.

At last the people began to think it must be a fairy; for what else could it be? – and no hurt nor harm was iver put an the white throut, until some wicked sinners of sojers kem to these parts, and laughed at all the people, and gibed and jeered them for thinkin' o' the likes; and one o' them in partic'lar (bad luck to him; God forgi' me for saying it!) swore he'd catch the throut and ate it for his dinner – the blackguard!

Well, what would you think o' the villainy of the sojer? Sure enough he cotch the throut, and away wid him home, and puts an the fryin'-pan, and into it he pitches the purty little thing. The throut squeeled all as one as a christian crathur, and, my dear, you'd think the sojer id split

THE WHITE TROUT

his sides laughin' – for he was a harden'd villain; and when he thought one side was done, he turns it over to fry the other; and, what would you think, but the divil a taste of a burn was an it at all at all; and sure the sojer thought it was a quare throut that could not be briled. 'But,' says he, 'I'll give it another turn by-and-by,' little thinkin' what was in store for him, the haythen.

Well, when he thought that side was done he turns it agin, and lo and behould you, the divil a taste more done that side was nor the other. 'Bad luck to me,' says the sojer, 'but that bates the world,' says he; 'but I'll thry you agin, my darlint,' says he, 'as cunnin' as you think yourself"; and so with that he turns it over and over, but not a sign of the fire was on the purty throut. 'Well,' says the desperate villain – (for sure, sir, only he was a desperate villain entirely, he might know he was doing a wrong thing, seein' that all his endeavours was no good) – 'Well,' says he, 'my jolly little throut, maybe you're fried enough, though you don't seem over well dress'd; but you may be better than you look, like a singed cat, and a tit-bit afther all,' says he; and with that he ups with his knife and fork to taste a piece o' the throut; but, my jew'l, the minit he puts his knife into the fish, there was a murtherin' screech, that you'd think the life id lave you if you hurd it, and away jumps the throut out av the fryin'-pan into the middle o' the flure; and an the spot where it fell, up riz a lovely lady – the beautifullest crathur that eyes ever seen, dressed in white, and a band o' goold in her hair, and a sthrame o' blood runnin' down her arm.

'Look where you cut me, you villain,' says she, and she held out her arm to him – and, my dear, he thought the sight id lave his eyes.

'Couldn't you lave me cool and comfortable in the river where you snared me, and not disturb me in my duty?' says she.

Well, he thrimbled like a dog in a wet sack, and at last he stammered out somethin', and begged for his life, and ax'd her ladyship's pardin, and said he didn't know she was on duty, or he was too good a sojer not to know betther nor to meddle wid her.

'I was on duty, then,' says the lady; 'I was watchin' for my true love that is comin' by wather to me,' says she, 'an' if he comes while I'm away, an' that I miss iv him, I'll turn you into a pinkeen, and I'll hunt

37

THE MAGICAL FOLK OF IRELAND

you up and down for evermore, while grass grows or wather runs.'

Well the sojer thought the life id lave him, at the thoughts iv his bein' turned into a pinkeen, and begged for mercy; and with that says the lady –

'Renounce your evil coorses,' says she, 'you villain, or you'll repint it too late; be a good man for the futhur, and go to your duty[1] reg'lar, and now,' says she, 'take me back and put me into the river again, where you found me.'

'Oh, my lady,' says the sojer, 'how could I have the heart to drownd a beautiful lady like you?'

But before he could say another word, the lady was vanished, and there he saw the little throut an the ground. Well he put it in a clean plate, and away he runs for the bare life, for fear her lover would come while she was away; and he run, and he run, even till he came to the cave agin, and threw the throut into the river. The minit he did, the wather was as red as blood for a little while, by rayson av the cut, I suppose, until the sthrame washed the stain away; and to this day there's a little red mark an the throut's side, where it was cut.[2]

Well, sir, from that day out the sojer was an altered man, and reformed his ways, and went to his duty reg'lar, and fasted three times a-week – though it was never fish he tuk an fastin' days, for afther the fright he got, fish id never rest an his stomach – savin' your presence.

But anyhow, he was an altered man, as I said before, and in coorse o' time he left the army, and turned hermit at last; and they say he *used to pray evermore for the soul of the White Throut.*

[These trout stories are common all over Ireland. Many holy wells are haunted by such blessed trout. There is a trout in a well on the border of Lough Gill, Sligo, that some paganish person put once on the gridiron. It carries the marks to this day. Long ago, the saint who sanctified the well put that trout there. Nowadays it is only visible to the pious, who have done due penance.]

1 The Irish peasant calls his attendance at the confessional 'going to his duty'.
2 The fish has really a red spot on its side.

THE LEGEND OF KNOCKGRAFTON

T. Crofton Croker

There was once a poor man who lived in the fertile glen of Aherlow, at the foot of the gloomy Galtee mountains, and he had a great hump on his back: he looked just as if his body had been rolled up and placed upon his shoulders; and his head was pressed down with the weight so much that his chin, when he was sitting, used to rest upon his knees for support. The country people were rather shy of meeting him in any lonesome place, for though, poor creature, he was as harmless and as inoffensive as a new-born infant, yet his deformity was so great that he scarcely appeared to be a human creature, and some ill-minded persons had set strange stories about him afloat. He was said to have a great knowledge of herbs and charms; but certain it was that he had a mighty skilful hand in plaiting straws and rushes into hats and baskets, which was the way he made his livelihood.

Lusmore, for that was the nickname put upon him by reason of his always wearing a sprig of the fairy cap, or lusmore (the foxglove), in his little straw hat, would ever get a higher penny for his plaited work than anyone else, and perhaps that was the reason why someone, out of envy, had circulated the strange stories about him. Be that as it may, it happened that he was returning one evening from the pretty town of Cahir towards Cappagh, and as little Lusmore walked very slowly, on account of the great hump upon his back, it was quite dark when he came to .the old moat of Knockgrafton, which stood on the right-hand side of his road. Tired and weary was he, and noways comfortable in his own mind at thinking how much farther he had to travel, and that he should be walking all the night; so he sat down under the moat to rest himself, and began looking mournfully enough upon the moon, which –

THE MAGICAL FOLK OF IRELAND

'Rising in clouded majesty, at length
Apparent Queen, unveil'd her peerless light.
And o'er the dark her silver mantle threw.'

Presently there rose a wild strain of unearthly melody upon the ear of little Lusmore; he listened, and he thought that he had never heard such ravishing music before. It was like the sound of many voices, each mingling and blending with the other so strangely that they seemed to be one, though all singing different strains, and the words of the song were these –

Da Luan, Da Mort, Da Luan, Da Mort, Da Luan, Da Mort;

when there would be a moment's pause, and then the round of melody went on again.

Lusmore listened attentively, scarcely drawing his breath lest he might lose the slightest note. He now plainly perceived that the singing was within the moat; and though at first it had charmed him so much, he began to get tired of hearing the same round sung over and over so often without any change; so availing himself of the pause when *Da Luan, Da Mort,* had been sung three times, he took up the tune, and raised it with the words *augus Da Dardeen*, and then went on singing with the voices inside of the moat. *Da Luan, Da Mort,* finishing the melody, when the pause again came, with *augus Da Dardeen*.

The fairies within Knockgrafton, for the song was a fairy melody, when they heard this addition to the tune, were so much delighted that, with instant resolve, it was determined to bring the mortal among them, whose musical skill so far exceeded theirs, and little Lusmore was conveyed into their company with the eddying speed of a whirlwind.

Glorious to behold was the sight that burst upon him as he came down through the moat, twirling round and round, with the lightness of a straw, to the sweetest music that kept time to his motion. The greatest honour was then paid him, for he was put above all the musicians, and he had servants tending upon him, and everything to his heart's

THE LEGEND OF KNOCKGRAFTON

content, and a hearty welcome to all; and, in short, he was made as much of as if he had been the first man in the land.

Presently Lusmore saw a great consultation going forward among the fairies, and, notwithstanding all their civility, he felt very much frightened, until one stepping out from the rest came up to him and said –

'Lusmore! Lusmore!
Doubt not, nor deplore,
For the hump which you bore
On your back is no more;
Look down on the floor,
And view it, Lusmore!'

When these words were said, poor little Lusmore felt himself so light, and so happy, that he thought he could have bounded at one jump over the moon, like the cow in the history of the cat and the fiddle; and he saw, with inexpressible pleasure, his hump tumble down upon the ground from his shoulders. He then tried to lift up his head, and he did so with becoming caution, fearing that he might knock it against the ceiling of the grand hall, where he was; he looked round and round again with the greatest wonder and delight upon everything, which appeared more and more beautiful; and, overpowered at beholding such a resplendent scene, his head grew dizzy, and his eyesight became dim. At last he fell into a sound sleep, and when he awoke he found that it was broad daylight, the sun shining brightly, and the birds singing sweetly; and that he was lying just at the foot of the moat of Knockgrafton, with the cows and sheep grazing peaceably round about him. The first thing Lusmore did, after saying his prayers, was to put his hand behind to feel for his hump, but no sign of one was there on his back, and he looked at himself with great pride, for he had now become a well-shaped dapper little fellow, and more than that, found himself in a full suit of new clothes, which he concluded the fairies, had made for him.

Towards Cappagh he went, stepping out as lightly, and springing up at every step as if he had been all his life a dancing-master. Not a creature who met Lusmore knew him without his hump, and he had a great work to persuade every one that he was the same man – in truth he was not, so far as the outward appearance went.

Of course it was not long before the story of Lusmore's hump got about, and a great wonder was made of it. Through the country, for miles round, it was the talk of every one, high and low.

One morning, as Lusmore was sitting contented enough at his cabin door, up came an old woman to him, and asked him if he could direct her to Cappagh.

'I need give you no directions, my good woman,' said Lusmore, 'for this is Cappagh; and whom may you want here?'

'I have come,' said the woman, 'out of Decie's country, in the county of Waterford, looking after one Lusmore, who, I have heard tell, had his hump taken off by the fairies; for there is a son of a gossip of mine who has got a hump on him that will be his death; and maybe, if he could use the same charm as Lusmore, the hump may be taken off him. And now I have told you the reason of my coming so far: 'tis to find out about this charm, if I can.'

Lusmore, who was ever a good-natured little fellow, told the woman all the particulars, how he had raised the tune for the fairies at Knockgrafton, how his hump had been removed from his shoulders, and how he had got a new suit of clothes into the bargain.

The woman thanked him very much, and then went away quite happy and easy in her own mind. When she came back to her gossip's house, in the county of Waterford, she told her everything that Lusmore had said, and they put the little hump-backed man, who was a peevish and cunning creature from his birth, upon a car, and took him all the way across the country. It was a long journey, but they did not care for that, so the hump was taken from off him; and they brought him, just at nightfall, and left him under the old moat of Knockgrafton.

Jack Madden, for that was the humpy man's name, had not been sitting there long when he heard the tune going on within the moat much sweeter than before; for the fairies were singing it the way Lusmore had settled their music for them, and the song was going on: *Da Luan, Da Mort, Da Luan, Da Mort, Da Luan, Da Mort, augus Da Dardeen*, without ever stopping. Jack Madden, who was in a great

THE LEGEND OF KNOCKGRAFTON

hurry to get quit of his hump, never thought of waiting until the fairies had done, or watching for a fit opportunity to raise the tune higher again than Lusmore had; so having heard them sing it over seven times without stopping, out he bawls, never minding the time or the humour of the tune, or how he could bring his words in properly, *augus Da Dardeen*, *augus Da Hena*, thinking that if one day was good, two were better; and that if Lusmore had one new suit of clothes given him, he should have two.

No sooner had the words passed his lips than he was taken up and whisked into the moat with prodigious force; and the fairies came crowding round about him with great anger, screeching and screaming, and roaring out, 'Who spoiled our tune? who spoiled our tune?' and one stepped up to him above all the rest, and said –

> 'Jack Madden! Jack Madden!
> Your words came so bad in
> The tune we felt glad in; –
> This castle you're had in,
> That your life we may sadden;
> Here's two humps for Jack Madden!'

And twenty of the strongest fairies brought Lusmore's hump, and put it down upon poor Jack's back, over his own, where it became fixed as firmly as if it was nailed on with twelve-penny nails, by the best carpenter that ever drove one. Out of their castle they then kicked him; and in the morning, when Jack Madden's mother and her gossip came to look after their little man, they found him half dead, lying at the foot of the moat, with the other hump upon his back. Well to be sure, how they did look at each other! but they were afraid to say anything, lest a hump might be put upon their own shoulders. Home they brought the unlucky Jack Madden with them, as downcast in their hearts and their looks as ever two gossips were; and what through the weight of his other hump, and the long journey, he died soon after, leaving, they say, his heavy curse to anyone who would go to listen to fairy tunes again.

A DONEGAL FAIRY

Letitia Maclintock

Ay, it's a bad thing to displeasure the gentry, sure enough – they can be unfriendly if they're angered, an' they can be the very best o' gude neighbours if they're treated kindly.

My mother's sister was her lone in the house one day, wi' a' big pot o' water boiling on the fire, and ane o' the wee folk fell down the chimney, and slipped wi' his leg in the hot water.

He let a terrible squeal out o' him, an' in a minute the house was full o' wee crathurs pulling him out o' the pot, an' carrying him across the floor.

'Did she scald you?' my aunt heard them saying to him.

'Na, na, it was mysel' scalded my ainsel',' quoth the wee fellow.

'A weel, a weel,' says they. 'If it was your ainsel scalded yoursel', we'll say nothing, but if she had scalded you, we'd ha' made her pay.'

CHANGELINGS

Sometimes the fairies fancy mortals, and carry them away into their own country, leaving instead some sickly fairy child, or a log of wood so bewitched that it seems to be a mortal pining away, and dying, and being buried. Most commonly they steal children. If you 'over look a child' – that is, look on it with envy – the fairies have it in their power. Many things can be done to find out in a child a changeling, but there is one infallible thing – lay it on the fire with this formula, 'Burn, burn, burn – if of the devil, burn; but if of God and the saints, be safe from harm' (given by Lady Wilde). Then if it be a changeling it will rush up the chimney with a cry, for, according to Giraldus Cambrensis, 'fire is the greatest of enemies to every sort of phantom, in so much that those who have seen apparitions fall into a swoon as soon as they are sensible of the brightness of fire.'

Sometimes the creature is got rid of in a more gentle way. It is on record that once when a mother was leaning over a wizened changeling the latch lifted and a fairy came in, carrying home again the wholesome stolen baby. 'It was the others,' she said, 'who stole it.' As for her, she wanted her own child.

Those who are carried away are happy, according to some accounts, having plenty of good living and music and mirth. Others say, however, that they are continually longing for their earthly friends. Lady Wilde gives a gloomy tradition that there are two kinds of fairies – one kind merry and gentle, the other evil, and sacrificing every year a life to Satan, for which purpose they steal mortals. No other Irish writer gives this tradition – if such fairies there be, they must be among the solitary spirits – Pookas, Fir Darrigs, and the like.

THE BREWERY OF EGG-SHELLS

T. Crofton Croker

Mrs Sullivan fancied that her youngest child had been exchanged by 'fairies theft', and certainly appearances warranted such a conclusion; for in one night her healthy, blue-eyed boy had become shrivelled up into almost nothing, and never ceased squalling and crying. This naturally made poor Mrs Sullivan very unhappy; and all the neighbours, by way of comforting her, said that her own child was, beyond any kind of doubt, with the good people, and that one of themselves was put in his place.

Mrs Sullivan of course could not disbelieve what everyone told her, but she did not wish to hurt the thing; for although its face was so withered, and its body wasted away to a mere skeleton, it had still a strong resemblance to her own boy. She, therefore, could not find it in her heart to roast it alive on the griddle, or to burn its nose off with the red-hot tongs, or to throw it out in the snow on the road-side, notwithstanding these, and several like proceedings, were strongly recommended to her for the recovery of her child.

One day who should Mrs Sullivan meet but a cunning woman, well known about the country by the name of Ellen Leah (or Grey Ellen). She had the gift, however she got it, of telling where the dead were, and what was good for the rest of their souls; and could charm away warts and wens, and do a great many wonderful things of the same nature.

'You're in grief this morning, Mrs Sullivan,' were the first words of Ellen Leah to her.

'You may say that, Ellen,' said Mrs Sullivan, 'and good cause I have to be in grief, for there was my own fine child whipped off from me out of his cradle, without as much as "by your leave" or "ask your

THE BREWERY OF EGG-SHELLS

pardon", and an ugly dony bit of a shrivelled-up fairy put in his place; no wonder, then, that you see me in grief, Ellen."

'Small blame to you, Mrs Sullivan,' said Ellen Leah, 'but are you sure 'tis a fairy?'

'Sure!' echoed Mrs Sullivan, 'sure enough I am to my sorrow, and can I doubt my own two eyes? Every mother's soul must feel for me!'

'Will you take an old woman's advice?' said Ellen Leah, fixing her wild and mysterious gaze upon the unhappy mother; and, after a pause, she added, 'but maybe you'll call it foolish?'

'Can you get me back my child, my own child, Ellen?' said Mrs Sullivan with great energy.

'If you do as I bid you,' returned Ellen Leah, 'you'll know.' Mrs Sullivan was silent in expectation, and Ellen continued, 'Put down the big pot, full of water, on the fire, and make it boil like mad; then get a dozen new-laid eggs, break them, and keep the shells, but throw away the rest; when that is done, put the shells in the pot of boiling water, and you will soon know whether it is your own boy or a fairy. If you find that it is a fairy in the cradle, take the red-hot poker and cram it down his ugly throat, and you will not have much trouble with him after that, I promise you.'

Home went Mrs Sullivan, and did as Ellen Leah desired. She put the pot on the fire, and plenty of turf under it, and set the water boiling at such a rate, that if ever water was red-hot, it surely was.

The child was lying, for a wonder, quite easy and quiet in the cradle, every now and then cocking his eye, that would twinkle as keen as a star in a frosty night, over at the great fire, and the big pot upon it; and he looked on with great attention at Mrs Sullivan breaking the eggs and putting down the egg-shells to boil. At last he asked, with the voice of a very old man, 'What are you doing, mammy?'

Mrs Sullivan's heart, as she said herself, was up in her mouth ready to choke her, at hearing the child speak. But she contrived to put the poker in the fire, and to answer, without making any wonder at the words, 'I'm brewing, *a vick*' (my son).

'And what are you brewing, mammy?' said the little imp, whose

47

THE MAGICAL FOLK OF IRELAND

supernatural gift of speech now proved beyond question that he was a fairy substitute.

'I wish the poker was red,' thought Mrs Sullivan; but it was a large one, and took a long time heating; so she determined to keep him in talk until the poker was in a proper state to thrust down his throat, and therefore repeated the question.

'Is it what I'm brewing, *a vick*,' said she, 'you want to know?'

'Yes, mammy: what are you brewing?' returned the fairy.

'Egg-shells, *a vick*,' said Mrs Sullivan.

'Oh!' shrieked the imp, starting up in the cradle, and clapping his hands together, 'I'm fifteen hundred years in the world, and I never saw a brewery of egg-shells before!' The poker was by this time quite red, and Mrs Sullivan, seizing it, ran furiously towards the cradle; but somehow or other her foot slipped, and she fell flat on the floor, and the poker flew out of her hand to the other end of the house. However, she got up without much loss of time and went to the cradle, intending to pitch the wicked thing that was in it into the pot of boiling water, when there she saw her own child in a sweet sleep, one of his soft round arms rested upon the pillow – his features were as placid as if their repose had never been disturbed, save the rosy mouth, which moved with a gentle and regular breathing.

JAMIE FREEL AND THE YOUNG LADY

A Donegal Tale

Miss Letitia Maclintock

Down in Fannet, in times gone by, lived Jamie Freel and his mother. Jamie was the widow's sole support; his strong arm worked for her untiringly, and as each Saturday night came round, he poured his wages into her lap, thanking her dutifully for the halfpence which she returned him for tobacco.

He was extolled by his neighbours as the best son ever known or heard of. But he had neighbours, of whose opinion he was ignorant – neighbours who lived pretty close to him, whom he had never seen, who are, indeed, rarely seen by mortals, except on May eves and Halloweens.

An old ruined castle, about a quarter of a mile from his cabin, was said to be the abode of the 'wee folk'. Every Halloween were the ancient windows lighted up, and passers-by saw little figures flitting to and fro inside the building, while they heard the music of pipes and flutes.

It was well known that fairy revels took place; but nobody had the courage to intrude on them.

Jamie had often watched the little figures from a distance, and listened to the charming music, wondering what the inside of the castle was like; but one Halloween he got up and took his cap, saying to his mother, 'I'm awa' to the castle to seek my fortune.'

'What!' cried she, 'would you venture there? you that's the poor

THE MAGICAL FOLK OF IRELAND

widow's one son! Dinna be sae venturesome an' foolitch, Jamie! They'll kill you, an' then what'll come o' me?'

'Never fear, mother; nae harm 'ill happen me, but I maun gae.'

He set out, and as he crossed the potato-field, came in sight of the castle, whose windows were ablaze with light, that seemed to turn the russet leaves, still clinging to the crabtree branches, into gold.

Halting in the grove at one side of the ruin, he listened to the elfin revelry, and the laughter and singing made him all the more determined to proceed.

Numbers of little people, the largest about the size of a child of five years old, were dancing to the music of flutes and fiddles, while others drank and feasted.

'Welcome, Jamie Freel! welcome, welcome, Jamie!' cried the company, perceiving their visitor. The word 'Welcome' was caught up and repeated by every voice in the castle.

Time flew, and Jamie was enjoying himself very much, when his hosts said, 'We're going to ride to Dublin tonight to steal a young lady. Will you come too, Jamie Freel?'

'Ay, that will I!' cried the rash youth, thirsting for adventure.

A troop of horses stood at the door. Jamie mounted, and his steed rose with him into the air. He was presently flying over his mother's cottage, surrounded by the elfin troop, and on and on they went, over bold mountains, over little hills, over the deep Lough Swilley, over towns and cottages, when people were burning nuts, and eating apples, and keeping merry Halloween. It seemed to Jamie that they flew all round Ireland before they got to Dublin.

'This is Derry,' said the fairies, flying over the cathedral spire; and what was said by one voice was repeated by all the rest, till fifty little voices were crying out, 'Derry! Derry! Derry!'

In like manner was Jamie informed as they passed over each town on the rout, and at length he heard the silvery voices cry, 'Dublin! Dublin!'

It was no mean dwelling that was to be honoured by the fairy visit, but one of the finest houses in Stephen's Green.

The troop dismounted near a window, and Jamie saw a beautiful

JAMIE FREEL AND THE YOUNG LADY

face, on a pillow in a splendid bed. He saw the young lady lifted and carried away, while the stick which was dropped in her place on the bed took her exact form.

The lady was placed before one rider and carried a short way, then given another, and the names of the towns were cried out as before.

They were approaching home. Jamie heard 'Rathmullan', 'Milford', 'Tamney', and then he knew they were near his own house.

'You've all had your turn at carrying the young lady,' said he. ''Why wouldn't I get her for a wee piece?'

'Ay, Jamie,' replied they, pleasantly, 'you may take your turn at carrying her, to be sure.'

Holding his prize very tightly, he dropped down near his mother's door.

'Jamie Freel, Jamie Freel! is that the way you treat us?' cried they, and they too dropped down near the door.

Jamie held fast, though he knew not what he was holding, for the little folk turned the lady into all sorts of strange shapes. At one moment she was a black dog, barking and trying to bite; at another, a glowing bar of iron, which yet had no heat; then, again, a sack of wool.

But still Jamie held her, and the baffled elves were turning away, when a tiny woman, the smallest of the party, exclaimed, 'Jamie Freel has her awa' frae us, but he shall hae nae gude o' her, for I'll mak' her deaf and dumb', and she threw something over the young girl.

While they rode off disappointed, Jamie lifted the latch and went in.

'Jamie, man!' cried his mother, 'you've been awa' all night; what have they done on you?'

'Naething bad, mother; I ha' the very best of gude luck. Here's a beautiful young lady I ha' brought you for company.

'Bless us an' save us!' exclaimed the mother, and for some minutes she was so astonished that she could not think of anything else to say.

Jamie told his story of the night's adventure, ending by saying, 'Surely you wouldna have allowed me to let her gang with them to be lost forever?'

'But a *lady*, Jamie! How can a lady eat we'er poor diet, and live in we'er poor way? I ax you that, you foolitch fellow?'

'Weel, mother, sure it's better for her to be here nor over yonder,' and he pointed in the direction of the castle.

Meanwhile, the deaf and dumb girl shivered in her light clothing, stepping close to the humble turf fire.

'Poor crathur, she's quare and handsome! Nae wonder they set their hearts on her,' said the old woman, gazing at her guest with pity and admiration. 'We maun dress her first; but what, in the name o' fortune, hae I fit for the likes o' her to wear?'

She went to her press in 'the room', and took out her Sunday gown of brown drugget; she then opened a drawer, and drew forth a pair of white stockings, a long snowy garment of fine linen, and a cap, her 'dead dress', as she called it.

These articles of attire had long been ready for a certain triste ceremony, in which she would some day fill the chief part, and only saw the light occasionally, when they were hung out to air; but she was willing to give even these to the fair trembling visitor, who was turning in dumb sorrow and wonder from her to Jamie, and from Jamie back to her.

The poor girl suffered herself to be dressed, and then sat down on a 'creepie' in the chimney corner, and buried her face in her hands.

'What'll we do to keep up a lady like thou?' cried the old woman.

'I'll work for you both, mother,' replied the son.

'An' how could a lady live on we'er poor diet?' she repeated.

'I'll work for her,' was all Jamie's answer.

He kept his word. The young lady was very sad for a long time, and tears stole down her cheeks many an evening while the old woman spun by the fire, and Jamie made salmon nets, an accomplishment lately acquired by him, in hopes of adding to the comfort of his guest.

But she was always gentle, and tried to smile when she perceived them looking at her; and by degrees she adapted herself to their ways and mode of life. It was not very long before she began to feed the pig, mash potatoes and meal for the fowls, and knit blue worsted socks.

So a year passed, and Halloween came round again. 'Mother,' said Jamie, taking down his cap, 'I'm off to the ould castle to seek my fortune.'

'Are you mad, Jamie?' cried his mother, in terror; 'sure they'll kill you this time for what you done on them last year.'

JAMIE FREEL AND THE YOUNG LADY

Jamie made light of her fears and went his way.

As he reached the crab-tree grove, he saw bright lights in the castle windows as before, and heard loud talking. Creeping under the window, he heard the wee folk say, 'That was a poor trick Jamie Freel played us this night last year, when he stole the nice young lady from us.'

'Ay,' said the tiny woman, 'an' I punished him for it, for there she sits, a dumb image by his hearth; but he does na' know that three drops out o' this glass I hold in my hand wad gie her her hearing and her speeches back again.'

Jamie's heart beat fast as he entered the hall. Again he was greeted by a chorus of welcomes from the company – 'Here comes Jamie Freel! welcome, welcome, Jamie!'

As soon as the tumult subsided, the little woman said, 'You be to drink our health, Jamie, out o' this glass in my hand.'

Jamie snatched the glass from her and darted to the door. He never knew how he reached his cabin, but he arrived there breathless, and sank on a stove by the fire.

'You're kilt surely this time, my poor boy,' said his mother.

'No, indeed, better luck than ever this time!' and he gave the lady three drops of the liquid that still remained at the bottom of the glass, notwithstanding his mad race over the potato-field.

The lady began to speak, and her first words were words of thanks to Jamie.

The three inmates of the cabin had so much to say to one another, that long after cock-crow, when the fairy music had quite ceased, they were talking round the fire.

'Jamie,' said the lady, 'be pleased to get me paper and pen and ink, that I may write to my father, and tell him what has become of me.'

She wrote, but weeks passed, and she received no answer. Again and again she wrote, and still no answer.

At length she said, 'You must come with me to Dublin, Jamie, to find my father.'

'I ha' no money to hire a car for you,' he replied, 'an' how can you travel to Dublin on your foot?'

THE MAGICAL FOLK OF IRELAND

But she implored him so much that he consented to set out with her, and walk all the way from Fannet to Dublin. It was not as easy as the fairy journey; but at last they rang the bell at the door of the house in Stephen's Green.

'Tell my father that his daughter is here,' said she to the servant who opened the door.

'The gentleman that lives here has no daughter, my girl. He had one, but she died better nor a year ago.'

'Do you not know me, Sullivan?'

'No, poor girl, I do not.'

'Let me see the gentleman. I only ask to see him.'

'Well, that's not much to ax; we'll see what can be done.'

In a few moments the Lady's father came to the door.

'Dear father,' said she, 'don't you know me?'

'How dare you call me your father?' cried the old gentleman, angrily. 'You are an impostor. I have no daughter.'

'Look in my face, father, and surely you'll remember me.'

'My daughter is dead and buried. She died a long, long time ago.' The old gentleman's voice changed from anger to sorrow. 'You can go,' he concluded.

'Stop, dear father, till you look at this ring on my finger. Look at your name and mine engraved on it.'

'It certainly is my daughter's ring; but I do not know how you came by it. I fear in no honest way.'

'Call my mother, she will be sure to know me,' said the poor girl, who, by this time, was crying bitterly,

'My poor wife is beginning to forget her sorrow. She seldom speaks of her daughter now. Why should I renew her grief by reminding her of her loss?'

But the young lady persevered, till at last the mother was sent for.

'Mother,' she began, when the old lady came to the door, 'don't you know your daughter?'

'I have no daughter; my daughter died and was buried a long, long time ago.'

'Only look in my face, and surely you'll know me.'

JAMIE FREEL AND THE YOUNG LADY

The old lady shook her head.

'You have all forgotten me; but look at this mole on my neck. Surely, mother, you know me now?'

'Yes, yes,' said the mother, 'my Gracie had a mole on her neck like that; but then I saw her in her coffin, and saw the lid shut down upon her.'

It became Jamie's turn to speak, and he gave the history of the fairy journey, of the theft of the young lady, of the figure he had seen laid in its place, of her life with his mother in Fannet, of last Halloween, and of the three drops that had released her from her enchantment.

She took up the story when he paused, and told how kind the mother and son had been to her.

The parents could not make enough of Jamie. They treated him with every distinction, and when he expressed his wish to return to Fannet, said they did not know what to do to show their gratitude.

But an awkward complication arose. The daughter would not let him go without her. 'If Jamie goes, I'll go too,' she said, 'He saved me from the fairies, and has worked for me ever since. If it had not been for him, dear father and mother, you would never have seen me again. If he goes, I'll go too.'

This being her resolution, the old gentleman said that Jamie should become his son-in-law. The mother was brought from Fannet in a coach and four, and there was a splendid wedding.

They all lived together in the grand Dublin house, and Jamie was heir to untold wealth at his father-in-law's death.

THE STOLEN CHILD

W. B. Yeats

Where dips the rocky highland
    Of Sleuth Wood in the lake,
There lies a leafy island
    Where flapping herons wake
The drowsy water-rats.
There we've hid our fairy vats
Full of berries,
And of reddest stolen cherries.
Come away, O, human child!
To the woods and waters wild,
With a fairy hand in hand,
For the world's more full of weeping than
        you can understand.

Where the wave of moonlight glosses
    The dim grey sands with light,
Far off by furthest Rosses
    We foot it all the night,
Weaving olden dances,
Mingling hands, and mingling glances.
    Till the moon has taken flight;
To and fro we leap,
    And chase the frothy bubbles,
    While the world is full of troubles,
And is anxious in its sleep.
Come away! O, human child!
To the woods and waters wild,

THE STOLEN CHILD

With a fairy hand in hand,
For the world's more full of weeping than
      you can understand.

Where the wandering water gushes
    From the hills above Glen-Car,
In pools among the rushes.
    That scarce could bathe a star,
We seek for slumbering trout,
    And whispering in their ears;
      We give them evil dreams,
Leaning softly out
    From ferns that drop their tears
      Of dew on the young streams.
Come! O, human child!
To the woods and waters wild,
With a fairy hand in hand,
For the world's more full of weeping than
      you can understand.

Away with us, he's going,
    The solemn-eyed;
He'll hear no more the lowing
    Of the calves on the warm hill-side.
Or the kettle on the hob
    Sing peace into his breast;
Or see the brown mice bob
    Round and round the oatmeal chest.
For he comes, the human child,
To the woods and waters wild,
With a fairy hand in hand,
For the world's more full of weeping than
      he can understand.

THE MERROW

The Merrow, or if you write it in the Irish, *Moruadh* or *Murrúghach*, from *muir*, sea, and *oigh*, a maid, is not uncommon, they say, on the wilder coasts. The fishermen do not like to see them, for it always means coming gales. The male *Merrows* (if you can use such a phrase – I have never heard the masculine of *Merrow*) have green teeth, green hair, pig's eyes, and red noses; but their women are beautiful, for all their fish tails and the little duck-like scale between their fingers. Sometimes they prefer, small blame to them, good-looking fishermen to their sea lovers. Near Bantry, in the last century, there is said to have been a woman covered all over with scales like a fish, who was descended from such a marriage. Sometimes they come out of the sea, and wander about the shore in the shape of little hornless cows. They have, when in their own shape, a red cap, called a *cohullen druith*, usually covered with feathers. If this is stolen, they cannot again go down under the waves.

Red is the colour of magic in every country, and has been so from the very earliest times. The caps of fairies and magicians are well-nigh always red.

THE SOUL CAGES

T. Crofton Croker

Jack Dogherty lived on the coast of the county Clare. Jack was a fisherman, as his father and grandfather before him had been. Like them, too, he lived all alone (but for the wife), and just in the same spot. People used to wonder why the Dogherty family were so fond of that wild situation, so far away from all human kind, and in the midst of huge shattered rocks, with nothing but the wide ocean to look upon. But they had their own good reasons for it.

The place was just the only spot on that part of the coast where anybody could well live. There was a neat little creek, where a boat might lie as snug as a puffin in her nest, and out from this creek a ledge of sunken rocks ran into the sea. Now when the Atlantic, according to custom, was raging with a storm, and a good westerly wind was blowing strong on the coast, many a richly laden ship went to pieces on these rocks; and then the fine bales of cotton and tobacco, and such like things, and the pipes of wine, and the puncheons of rum, and the casks of brandy, and the kegs of Hollands that used to come ashore! Dunbeg Bay was just like a little estate to the Doghertys.

Not but they were kind and humane to a distressed sailor, if ever one had the good luck to get to land; and many a time indeed did Jack put out in his little *corragh* (which, though not quite equal to honest Andrew Hennessy's canvas life-boat, would breast the billows like any gannet), to lend a hand towards bringing off the crew from a wreck. But when the ship had gone to pieces, and the crew were all lost, who would blame Jack for picking up all he could find?

'And who is the worse of it?' said he. 'For as to the king, God bless him! everybody knows he's rich enough already without getting what's floating in the sea.'

THE MAGICAL FOLK OF IRELAND

Jack, though such a hermit, was a good-natured, jolly fellow. No other, sure, could ever have coaxed Biddy Mahony to quit her father's snug and warm house in the middle of the town of Ennis, and to go so many miles off to live among the rocks, with the seals and sea-gulls for next-door neighbours. But Biddy knew that Jack was the man for a woman who wished to be comfortable and happy; for, to say nothing of the fish, Jack had the supplying of half the gentlemen's houses of the country with the Godsends that came into the bay. And she was right in her choice; for no woman ate, drank, or slept better, or made a prouder appearance at chapel on Sundays, than Mrs Dogherty.

Many a strange sight, it may well be supposed, did Jack see, and many a strange sound did he hear, but nothing daunted him. So far was he from being afraid of Merrows, or such beings, that the very first wish of his heart was to fairly meet with one. Jack had heard that they were mighty like Christians, and that luck had always come out of an acquaintance with them. Never, therefore, did he dimly discern the Merrows moving along the face of the waters in their robes of mist, but he made direct for them; and many a scolding did Biddy, in her own quiet way, bestow upon Jack for spending his whole day out at sea, and bringing home no fish. Little did poor Biddy know the fish Jack was after!

It was rather annoying to Jack that, though living in a place where the Merrows were as plenty as lobsters, he never could get a right view of one. What vexed him more was that both his father and grandfather had often and often seen them; and he even remembered hearing, when a child, how his grandfather, who was the first of the family that had settled down at the creek, had been so intimate with a Merrow that, only for fear of vexing the priest, he would have had him stand for one of his children. This, however, Jack did not well know how to believe.

Fortune at length began to think that it was only right that Jack should know as much as his father and grandfather did. Accordingly, one day when he had strolled a little farther than usual along the coast to the northward, just as he turned a point, he saw something, like to nothing he had ever seen before, perched upon a rock at a little distance out to sea. It looked green in the body, as well as he could

THE SOUL CAGES

discern at that distance, and he would have sworn, only the thing was impossible, that it had a cocked hat in its hand. Jack stood for a good half-hour straining his eyes, and wondering at it, and all the time the thing did not stir hand or foot. At last Jack's patience was quite worn out, and he gave a loud whistle and a hail, when the Merrow (for such it was) started up, put the cocked hat on its head, and dived down, head foremost, from the rock.

Jack's curiosity was now excited, and he constantly directed his steps towards the point; still he could never get a glimpse of the sea-gentleman with the cocked hat; and with thinking and thinking about the matter, he began at last to fancy he had been only dreaming. One very rough day, however, when the sea was running mountains high, Jack Dogherty determined to give a look at the Merrow's rock (for he had always chosen a fine day before), and then he saw the strange thing cutting capers upon the top of the rock, and then diving down, and then coming up, and then diving down again.

Jack had now only to choose his time (that is, a good blowing day), and he might see the man of the sea as often as he pleased. All this, however, did not satisfy him – 'much will have more'; he wished now to get acquainted with the Merrow, and even in this he succeeded. One tremendous blustering day, before he got to the point whence he had a view of the Merrow's rock, the storm came on so furiously that Jack was obliged to take shelter in one of the caves which are so numerous along the coast; and there, to his astonishment, he saw sitting before him a thing with green hair, long green teeth, a red nose, and pig's eyes. It had a fish's tail, legs with scales on them, and short arms like fins. It wore no clothes, but had the cocked hat under its arm, and seemed engaged thinking very seriously about something.

Jack, with all his courage, was a little daunted; but now or never, thought he; so up he went boldly to the cogitating fishman, took off his hat, and made his best bow.

'Your servant, sir,' said Jack.

'Your servant, kindly, Jack Dogherty,' answered the Merrow.

'To be sure, then, how well your honour knows my name!' said Jack.

THE MAGICAL FOLK OF IRELAND

'Is it I not know your name, Jack Dogherty? Why, man, I knew your grandfather long before he was married to Judy Regan, your grandmother! Ah, Jack, Jack, I was fond of that grandfather of yours; he was a mighty worthy man in his time: I never met his match above or below, before or since, for sucking in a shellful of brandy. I hope, my boy,' said the old fellow, with a merry twinkle in his eyes, 'I hope you're his own grandson!'

'Never fear me for that,' said Jack; 'if my mother had only reared me on brandy, 'tis myself that would be a sucking infant to this hour!'

'Well, I like to hear you talk so manly; you and I must be better acquainted, if it were only for your grandfather's sake. But, Jack, that father of yours was not the thing! he had no head at all.'

'I'm sure,' said Jack, 'since your honour lives down under the water, you must be obliged to drink a power to keep any heat in you in such a cruel, damp, could place. Well, I've often heard of Christians drinking like fishes; and might I be so bold as ask where you get the spirits?'

'Where do you get them yourself, Jack?' said the Merrow, twitching his red nose between his forefinger and thumb.

'Hubbubboo,' cries Jack, 'now I see how it is; but I suppose, sir, your honour has got a fine dry cellar below to keep them in.'

'Let me alone for the cellar,' said the Merrow, with a knowing wink of his left eye.

'I'm sure,' continued Jack, 'it must be mighty well worth the looking at.'

'You may say that, Jack,' said the Merrow; 'and if you meet me here next Monday, just at this time of the day, we will have a little more talk with one another about the matter.'

Jack and the Merrow parted the best friends in the world.

On Monday they met, and Jack was not a little surprised to see that the Merrow had two cocked hats with him, one under each arm.

'Might I take the liberty to ask, sir,' said Jack, 'why your honour has brought the two hats with you today? You would not, sure, be going to give me one of them, to keep for the curiosity of the thing?'

'No, no, Jack,' said he, 'I don't get my hats so easily, to part with

THE SOUL CAGES

them that way; but I want you to come down and dine with me, and I brought you the hat to dine with.'

'Lord bless and preserve us!' cried Jack, in amazement, 'would you want me to go down to the bottom of the salt sea ocean? Sure, I'd be smothered and choked up with the water, to say nothing of being drowned! And what would poor Biddy do for me, and what would she say?'

'And what matter what she says, you *pinkeen*? Who cares for Biddy's squalling? It's long before your grandfather would have talked in that way. Many's the time he stuck that same hat on his head, and dived down boldly after me; and many's the snug bit of dinner and good shellful of brandy he and I have had together below, under the water.'

'Is it really, sir, and no joke?' said Jack; 'why, then, sorrow from me for ever and a day after, if I'll be a bit worse man nor my grandfather was! Here goes – but play me fair now. Here's neck or nothing!' cried Jack.

'That's your grandfather all over,' said the old fellow; 'so come along, then, and do as I do.'

They both left the cave, walked into the sea, and then swam a piece until they got to the rock. The Merrow climbed to the top of it, and Jack followed him. On the far side it was as straight as the wall of a house, and the sea beneath looked so deep that Jack was almost cowed.

'Now, do you see, Jack,' said the Merrow: 'just put this hat on your head, and mind to keep your eyes wide open. Take hold of my tail, and follow after me, and you'll see what you'll see.'

In he dashed, and in dashed Jack after him boldly.

They went and they went, and Jack thought they'd never stop going. Many a time did he wish himself sitting at home by the fireside with Biddy. Yet where was the use of wishing now, when he was so many miles, as he thought, below the waves of the Atlantic? Still he held hard by the Merrow's tail, slippery as it was; and, at last, to Jack's great surprise, they got out of the water, and he actually found himself on dry land at the bottom of the sea. They landed just in front of a nice house that was slated very neatly with oyster shells! and the Merrow, turning about to Jack, welcomed him down.

THE MAGICAL FOLK OF IRELAND

Jack could hardly speak, what with wonder, and what with being out of breath with travelling so fast through the water. He looked about him and could see no living things, barring crabs and lobsters, of which there were plenty walking leisurely about on the sand. Overhead was the sea like a sky, and the fishes like birds swimming about in it

'Why don't you speak, man?' said the Merrow: 'I dare say you had no notion that I had such a snug little concern here as this? Are you smothered, or choked, or drowned, or are you fretting after Biddy, eh?'

'Oh! not myself, indeed,' said Jack, showing his teeth with a good-humoured grin; 'but who in the world would ever have thought of seeing such a thing?'

'Well, come along, and let's see what they've got for us to eat?'

Jack really was hungry, and it gave him no small pleasure to perceive a fine column of smoke rising from the chimney, announcing what was going on within. Into the house he followed the Merrow, and there he saw a good kitchen, right well provided with everything. There was a noble dresser, and plenty of pots and pans, with two young Merrows cooking. His host then led him into the room, which was furnished shabbily enough. Not a table or a chair was there in it; nothing but planks and logs of wood to sit on, and eat off. There was, however, a good fire blazing upon the hearth – a comfortable sight to Jack.

'Come now, and I'll show you where I keep – you know what,' said the Merrow, with a sly look; and opening a little door, he led Jack into a fine cellar, well filled with pipes, and kegs, and hogsheads, and barrels.

'What do you say to that, Jack Dogherty? Eh! may be a body can't live snug under the water?'

'Never the doubt of that,' said Jack, with a convincing smack of his under lip, that he really thought what he said.

They went back to the room, and found dinner laid. There was no tablecloth, to be sure – but what matter? It was not always Jack had one at home. The dinner would have been no discredit to the first house of the country on a fast day. The choicest of fish, and no wonder, was there. Turbots, and sturgeons, and soles, and lobsters, and oysters, and twenty other kinds, were on the planks at once, and plenty of the best

THE SOUL CAGES

of foreign spirits. The wines, the old fellow said, were too cold for his stomach.

Jack ate and drank till he could eat no more: then, taking up a shell of brandy, 'Here's to your honour's good health, sir,' said he; 'though, begging you pardon, it's mighty odd that as long as we've been acquainted I don't know your name yet.'

'That's true. Jack,' replied he; 'I never thought of it before, but better late than never. My name's Coomara.'

'And a mighty decent name it is,' cried Jack, taking another shellfull: 'here's to your good health, Coomara, and may ye live these fifty years to come!'

'Fifty years!' repeated Coomara; 'I'm obliged to you, indeed! If you had said five hundred, it would have been something worth the wishing.'

'By the laws, sir,' cries jack, 'youz live to a powerful age here under the water! You knew my grandfather, and he's dead and gone better than these sixty years. I'm sure it must be a healthy place to live in.'

'No doubt of it; but come, Jack, keep the liquor stirring.'

Shell after shell did they empty, and to Jack's exceeding surprise, he found the drink never got into his head, owing, I suppose, to the sea being over them, which kept their noddles cool.

Old Coomara got exceedingly comfortable, and sung several songs; but Jack, if his life had depended on it, never could remember more than

> *'Rum fum boodle boo,*
> *Ripple dimple nitty dob;*
> *Dumdoo doodle coo,*
> *Raffle taffle chiitiboo!'*

It was the chorus to one of them; and, to say the truth, nobody that I know has ever been able to pick any particular meaning out of it; but that, to be sure, is the case with many a song nowadays.

At length said he to Jack, 'Now, my dear boy, if you follow me, I'll show you my *curiosities!*' He opened a little door, and led Jack into a large room, where Jack saw a great many odds and ends that Coomara had picked up at one time or another. What chiefly took his

THE MAGICAL FOLK OF IRELAND

attention, however, were things like lobster-pots ranged on the ground along the wall.

'Weil, Jack, how do you like my *curiosities*?' said old Coo.

'Upon my *sowkins*,[1] sir,' said Jack, 'they're mighty well worth the looking at; but might I make so bold as to ask what these things like lobster-pots are?'

'Oh! the Soul Cages, is it?'

'The what? sir!'

'These things here that I keep the souls in.'

'*Arrah*! what souls, sir?' said Jack, in amazement; 'sure the fish have no souls in them?'

'Oh! no,' replied Coo, quite coolly, 'that they have not; but these are the souls of drowned sailors.'

'The Lord preserve us from all harm!' muttered Jack, 'how in the world did you get them?'

'Easily enough: I've only, when I see a good storm coming on, to set a couple of dozen of these, and then, when the sailors are drowned and the souls get out of them under the water, the poor things are almost perished to death, not being used to the cold; so they make into my pots for shelter, and then I have them snug, and fetch them home, and keep them here dry and warm; and is it not well for them, poor souls, to get into such good quarters?'

Jack was so thunderstruck he did not know what to say, so he said nothing. They went back into the dining-room, and had a little more brandy, which was excellent, and then, as Jack knew that it must be getting late, and as Biddy might be uneasy, he stood up, and said he thought it was time for him to be on the road.

'Just as you like, Jack,' said Coo, 'but take a *duc an durrus*[2] before you go; you've a cold journey before you.'

Jack knew better manners than to refuse the parting glass. 'I wonder,' said he, 'will I be able to make out my way home?'

---

1 *Sowkins*, diminutive of soul.

2 *Recte, deoch an dorrus*, door-drink or stirrup-cup.

THE SOUL CAGES

'What should ail you,' said Coo, 'when I'll show you the way?'

Out they went before the house, and Coomara took one of the cocked hats, and put it upon Jack's head the wrong way, and then lifted him up on his shoulder that he might launch him up into the water.

'Now,' says he, giving him a heave, 'you'll come up just in the same spot you came down in; and, Jack, mind and throw me back the hat.'

He canted Jack off his shoulder, and up he shot like a bubble – whirr, whirr, whiz – away he went up through the water, till he came to the very rock he had jumped off, where he found a landing-place, and then in he threw the hat, which sunk like a stone.

The sun was just going down in the beautiful sky of a calm summer's evening. *Feascor* was seen dimly twinkling in the cloudless heaven, a solitary star, and the waves of the Atlantic flashed in a golden flood of light. So Jack, perceiving it was late, set off home; but when he got there, not a word did he say to Biddy of where he had spent his day.

The state of the poor souls cooped up in the lobster-pots gave Jack a great deal of trouble, and how to release them cost him a great deal of thought. He at first had a mind to speak to the priest about the matter. But what could the priest do, and what did Coo care for the priest? Besides, Coo was a good sort of an old fellow, and did not think he was doing any harm. Jack had a regard for him, too, and it also might not be much to his own credit if it were known that he used to go dine with Merrows. On the whole, he thought his best plan would be to ask Coo to dinner, and to make him drunk, if he was able, and then to take the hat and go down and turn up the pots. It was, first of all, necessary, however, to get Biddy out of the way; for Jack was prudent enough, as she was a woman, to wish to keep the thing secret from her.

Accordingly, Jack grew mighty pious all of a sudden, and said to Biddy that he thought it would be for the good of both their souls if she was to go and take her rounds at Saint John's Well, near Ennis. Biddy thought so too, and accordingly off she set one fine morning at day-dawn, giving Jack a strict charge to have an eye to the place. The coast being clear, away went Jack to the rock to give the appointed signal to Coomara, which was throwing a big stone into the water. Jack threw, and up sprang Coo!

THE MAGICAL FOLK OF IRELAND

'Good morning, Jack,' said he; 'what do you want with me?'

'Just nothing at all to speak about, sir,' returned Jack, 'only to come and take a bit of dinner wath me, if I might make so free as to ask you, and sure I'm now after doing so.'

'It's quite agreeable, Jack, I assure you; what's your hour?'

'Any time that's most convenient to you, sir – say one o'clock, that you may go home, if you wish, with the daylight.'

'I'll be with you,' said Coo, 'never fear me.'

Jack went home, and dressed a noble fish dinner, and got out plenty of his best foreign spirits, enough, for that matter, to make twenty men drunk. Just to the minute came Coo, with his cocked hat under his arm. Dinner was ready, they sat down, and ate and drank away manfully. Jack, thinking of the poor souls below in the pots, plied old Coo well with brandy, and encouraged him to sing, hoping to put him under the table, but poor Jack forgot that he had not the sea over his own head to keep it cool. The brandy got into it, and did his business for him, and Coo reeled off home, leaving his entertainer as dumb as a haddock on a Good Friday.

Jack never woke till the next morning, and then he was in a sad way. ''Tis to no use for me thinking to make that old Rapparee drunk,' said Jack, 'and how in this world can I help the poor souls out of the lobster-pots?' After ruminating nearly the whole day, a thought struck him. 'I have it,' says he, slapping his knee; 'I'll be sworn that Coo never saw a drop of *poteen*, as old as he is, and that's the thing to settle him! Oh! then, is not it well that Biddy will not be home these two days yet; I can have another twist at him.'

Jack asked Coo again, and Coo laughed at him for having no better head, telling him he'd never come up to his grandfather.

'Well, but try me again,' said Jack, 'and I'll be bail to drink you drunk and sober, and drunk again.'

'Anything in my power,' said Coo, 'to oblige you.'

At this dinner Jack took care to have his own liquor well watered, and to give the strongest brandy he had to Coo. At last says he, 'Pray, sir, did you ever drink any *poteen*? – any real mountain dew?'

'No,' says Coo; 'what's that, and where does it come from?'

THE SOUL CAGES

'Oh, that's a secret,' said Jack, 'but it's the right stuff – never believe me again, if 'tis not fifty times as good as brandy or rum either. Biddy's brother just sent me a present of a little drop, in exchange for some brandy, and as you're an old friend of the family, I kept it to treat you with.'

'Well, let's see what sort of thing it is,' said Coomara.

The *poteen* was the right sort. It was first-rate, and had the real smack upon it. Coo was delighted: he drank and he sung *Rum bum boodle boo* over and over again; and he laughed and he danced, till he fell on the floor fast asleep. Then Jack, who had taken good care to keep himself sober, snapt up the cocked hat – ran off to the rock – leaped in, and soon arrived at Coo's habitation.

All was as still as a churchyard at midnight – not a Merrow, old or young, was there. In he went and turned up the pots, but nothing did he see, only he heard a sort of a little whistle or chirp as he raised each of them. At this he was surprised, till he recollected what the priests had often said, that nobody living could see the soul, no more than they could see the wind or the air. Having now done all that he could do for them, he set the pots as they were before, and sent a blessing after the poor souls to speed them on their journey wherever they were going. Jack now began to think of returning; he put the hat on, as was right, the wrong way; but when he got out he found the water so high over his head that he had no hopes of ever getting up into it, now that he had not old Coomara to give him a lift. He walked about looking for a ladder, but not one could he find, and not a rock was there in sight. At last he saw a spot where the sea hung rather lower than anywhere else, so he resolved to try there. Just as he came to it, a big cod happened to put down his tail. Jack made a jump and caught hold of it, and the cod, all in amazement, gave a bounce and pulled Jack up. The minute the hat touched the water away Jack was whisked, and up he shot like a cork, dragging the poor cod, that he forgot to let go, up with him tail foremost. He got to the rock in no time, and without a moment's delay hurried home, rejoicing in the good deed he had done.

But, meanwhile, there was fine work at home; for our friend Jack had hardly left the house on his soul-freeing expedition, when back came Biddy from her soul-saving one to the well. When she entered the house and saw the things lying *thrie-na-helah*[3] on the table before her – 'Here's a pretty job!' said she; 'that blackguard of mine – what ill-luck I had ever to marry him! He has picked up some vagabond or other, while I was praying for the good of his soul, and they've been drinking all the *poteen* that my own brother gave him, and all the spirits, to be sure, that he was to have sold to his honour.' Then hearing an outlandish kind of a grunt, she looked down, and saw Coomara lying under the table. 'The blessed Virgin help me,' shouted she, 'if he has not made a real beast of himself! Well, well, I've often heard of a man making a beast of himself with drink! Oh hone, oh hone! – Jack, honey, what will I do with you, or what will I do without you? How can any decent woman ever think of living with a beast?'

With such like lamentations Biddy rushed out of the house, and was going she knew not where, when she heard the well-known voice of Jack singing a merry tune. Glad enough was Biddy to find him safe and sound, and not turned into a thing that was like neither fish nor flesh. Jack was obliged to tell her all, and Biddy, though she had half a mind to be angry with him for not telling her before, owned that he had done a great service to the poor souls. Back they both went most lovingly to the house, and Jack wakened up Coomara; and, perceiving the old fellow to be rather dull, he bid him not to be cast down, for 'twas many a good man's case; said it all came of his not being used to the *poteen*, and recommended him, by way of cure, to swallow a hair of the dog that bit him. Coo, however, seemed to think he had had quite enough. He got up, quite out of sorts, and without having the manners to say one word in the way of civility, he sneaked off to cool himself by a jaunt through the salt water.

Coomara never missed the souls. He and Jack continued the best friends in the world, and no one, perhaps, ever equalled Jack for freeing souls from purgatory; for he contrived fifty excuses for getting into the house below the sea, unknown to the old fellow, and then turning up

3 *Tri-na-cheile*, literally through other, i.e. higgledy-piggledy.

THE SOUL CAGES

the pots and letting out the souls. It vexed him, to be sure, that he could never see them; but as he knew the thing to be impossible, he was obliged to be satisfied.

Their intercourse continued for several years. However, one morning, on Jack's throwing in a stone as usual, he got no answer. He flung another, and another, still there was no reply. He went away, and returned the following morning, but it was to no purpose. As he was without the hat, he could not go down to see what had become of old Coo, but his belief was, that the old man, or the old fish, or whatever he was, had either died, or had removed from that part of the country.

FLORY CANTILLON'S FUNERAL

T. Crofton Croker

The ancient burial-place of the Cantillon family was on an island in Ballyheigh Bay. This island was situated at no great distance from the shore, and at a remote period was overflowed in one of the encroachments which the Atlantic has made on that part of the coast of Kerry. The fishermen declare they have often seen the ruined walls of an old chapel beneath them in the water, as they sailed over the clear green sea of a sunny afternoon. However this may be, it is well-known that the Cantillons were, like most other Irish families, strongly attached to their ancient burial-place; and this attachment led to the custom, when any of the family died, of carrying the corpse to the seaside, where the coffin was left on the shore within reach of the tide. In the morning it had disappeared, being, as was traditionally believed, conveyed away by the ancestors of the deceased to their family tomb.

Connor Crowe, a county Clare man, was related to the Cantillons by marriage. 'Connor Mac in Cruagh, of the seven quarters of Breintragh', as he was commonly called, and a proud man he was of the name. Connor, be it known, would drink a quart of salt water, for its medicinal virtues, before breakfast; and for the same reason, I suppose, double that quantity of raw whiskey between breakfast and night, which last he did with as little inconvenience to himself as any man in the barony of Moyferta; and were I to add Clanderalaw and Ibrickan, I don't think I should say wrong.

On the death of Florence Cantillon, Connor Crowe was determined to satisfy himself about the truth of this story of the old church under the sea: so when he heard the news of the old fellow's death, away with him to Ardfert, where Flory was laid out in high style, and a beautiful corpse he made.

FLORY CANTILLON'S FUNERAL

Flory had been as jolly and as rollicking a boy in his day as ever was stretched, and his wake was in every respect worthy of him. There was all kind of entertainment, and all sort of diversion at it, and no less than three girls got husbands there – more luck to them. Everything was as it should be; all that side of the country, from Dingle to Tarbert, was at the funeral. The Keen was sung long and bitterly; and, according to the family custom, the coffin was carried to Ballyheigh strand, where it was laid upon the shore, with a prayer for the repose of the dead.

The mourners departed, one group after another, and at last Connor Crowe was left alone. He then pulled out his whiskey bottle, his drop of comfort, as he called it, which he required, being in grief; and down he sat upon a big stone that was sheltered by a projecting rock, and partly concealed from view, to await with patience the appearance of the ghostly undertakers.

The evening came on mild and beautiful. He whistled an old air which he had heard in his childhood, hoping to keep idle fears out of his head; but the wild strain of that melody brought a thousand recollections with it, which only made the twilight appear more pensive.

'If 'twas near the gloomy tower of Dunmore, in my own sweet country, I was,' said Connor Crowe, with a sigh, 'one might well believe that the prisoners, who were murdered long ago there in the vaults under the castle, would be the hands to carry off the coffin out of envy, for never a one of them was buried decently, nor had as much as a coffin amongst them all. 'Tis often, sure enough, I have heard lamentations and great mourning coming from the vaults of Dunmore Castle; but,' continued he, after fondly pressing his lips to the mouth of his companion and silent comforter, the whiskey bottle, 'didn't I know all the time well enough, 'twas the dismal sounding waves working through the cliffs and hollows of the rocks, and fretting themselves to foam. Oh, then, Dunmore Castle, it is you that are the gloomy-looking tower on a gloomy day, with the gloomy hills behind you; when one has gloomy thoughts on their heart, and sees you like a ghost rising out of the smoke made by the kelp burners on the strand, there is, the Lord save us! as fearful a look about you as about the Blue Man's Lake at midnight. Well, then, anyhow,' said Connor, after a pause, 'is it not a blessed night, though surely the moon looks mighty pale in the face? St Senan himself between us and all kinds of harm.'

It was, in truth, a lovely moonlight night; nothing was to be seen around but the dark rocks, and the white pebbly beach, upon which the sea broke with a hoarse and melancholy murmur. Connor, notwithstanding his frequent draughts, felt rather queerish, and almost began to repent his curiosity. It was certainly a solemn sight to behold the black coffin resting upon the white strand. His imagination gradually converted the deep moaning of old ocean into a mournful wail for the dead, and from the shadowy recesses of the rocks he imaged forth strange and visionary forms.

As the night advanced, Connor became weary with watching. He caught himself, more than once in the act of nodding, when suddenly giving his head a shake, he would look towards the black coffin. But the narrow house of death remained unmoved before him.

It was long past midnight, and the moon was sinking into the sea, when he heard the sound of many voices, which gradually became stronger, above the heavy and monotonous roll of the sea. He listened, and presently could distinguish a Keen of exquisite sweetness, the notes of which rose and fell with the heaving of the waves, whose deep murmur mingled with and supported the strain!

The Keen grew louder and louder, and seemed to approach the beach, and then fell into a low, plaintive wail. As it ended Connor beheld a number of strange and, in the dim light, mysterious-looking figures emerge from the sea, and surround the coffin, which they prepared to launch into the water.

'This comes of marrying with the creatures of earth,' said one of the figures, in a clear, yet hollow tone.

'True,' replied another, with a voice still more fearful, 'our king would never have commanded his gnawing white-toothed waves to devour the rocky roots of the island cemetery, had not his daughter, Durfulla, been buried there by her mortal husband!'

'But the time will come,' said a third, bending over the coffin,

FLORY CANTILLON'S FUNERAL

'When mortal eye – our work shall spy,
And mortal ear – our dirge shall hear.'

'Then,' said a fourth, 'our burial of the Cantillons is at an end for ever!'

As this was spoken the coffin was borne from the beach by a retiring wave, and the company of sea people prepared to follow it; but at the moment one chanced to discover Connor Crowe, as fixed with wonder and as motionless with fear as the stone on which he sat.

'The time is come,' cried the unearthly being, 'the time is come; a human eye looks on the forms of ocean, a human ear has heard their voices. Farewell to the Cantillons; the sons of the sea are no longer doomed to bury the dust of the earth!'

One after the other turned slowly round, and regarded Connor Crowe, who still remained as if bound by a spell. Again arose their funeral song; and on the next wave they followed the coffin. The sound of the lamentation died away, and at length nothing was heard but the rush of waters. The coffin and the train of sea people sank over the old churchyard, and never since the funeral of old Flory Cantillon have any of the family been carried to the strand of Ballyheigh, for conveyance to their rightful burial-place, beneath the waves of the Atlantic.

THE SOLITARY FAIRIES

LEPRACAUN. CLURICAUN. FAR DARRIG.

'The name *Lepracaun*,' Mr Douglas Hyde writes to me, 'is from the Irish *leith brog* – i.e., the One-shoemaker, since he is generally seen working at a single shoe. It is spelt in Irish *leith bhrogan*, or *leith phrogan*, and is in some places pronounced Luchryman, as O'Kearney writes it in that very rare book, the *Feis Tigh Chonain*.'

The *Lepracaun*, *Cluricaun*, and *Far Darrig*. Are these one spirit in different moods and shapes? Hardly two Irish writers are agreed. In many things these three fairies, if three, resemble each other. They are withered, old, and solitary, in every way unlike the sociable spirits of the first sections. They dress with all unfairy homeliness, and are, indeed, most sluttish, slouching, jeering, mischievous phantoms. They are the great practical jokers among the good people

The *Lepracaun* makes shoes continually, and has grown very rich. Many treasure-crocks, buried of old in war-time, has he now for his own. In the early part of this century, according to Croker, in a newspaper office in Tipperary, they used to show a little shoe forgotten by a Lepracaun.

The *Cluricaun* (*Clobhair-ceann*, in O'Kearney) makes himself drunk in gentlemen's cellars. Some suppose he is merely the Lepracaun on a spree. He is almost unknown in Connaught and the north.

The *Far Darrig* (*fear dearg*), which means the Red Man, for he wears a red cap and coat, busies himself with practical joking, especially with

LEPRACAUN. CLURICAUN. FAR DARRIG

gruesome joking. This he does, and nothing else.

The *Fear-Gorta* (Man of Hunger) is an emaciated phantom that goes through the land in famine time, begging an alms and bringing good luck to the giver.

There are other solitary fairies, such as the House-spirit and the *Water-sheerie*, own brother to the English Jack-o'-Lantern; the *Pooka* and the *Banshee* – concerning these presently; the *Dallahan*, or headless phantom – one used to stand in a Sligo street on dark nights till lately; the Black Dog, a form, perhaps, of the *Pooka*. The ships at the Sligo quays are haunted sometimes by this spirit, who announces his presence by a sound like the flinging of all 'the tin porringers in the world' down into the hold. He even follows them to sea.

The *Leanhaun Shee* (fairy mistress) seeks the love of mortals. If they refuse, she must be their slave; if they consent, they are hers, and can only escape by finding another to take their place. The fairy lives on their life, and they waste away. Death is no escape from her. She is the Gaelic muse, for she gives inspiration to those she persecutes. The Gaelic poets die young, for she is restless, and will not let them remain long on earth – this malignant phantom.

Besides these are divers monsters – the *Augh-iska*, the Water-horse, the Payshtha (*píast=bestia*), the Lake-dragon, and such like; but whether these be animals, fairies, or spirits, I know not.

MASTER AND MAN

T. Crofton Croker

Billy Mac Daniel was once as likely a young man as ever shook his brogue at a patron,[1] emptied a quart, or handled a *shillelagh*; fearing for nothing but the want of drink; caring for nothing but who should pay for it; and thinking of nothing but how to make fun over it; drunk or sober, a word and a blow was ever the way with Billy Mac Daniel; and a mighty easy way it is of either getting into or of ending a dispute. More is the pity that, through the means of his thinking, and fearing, and caring for nothing, this same Billy Mac Daniel fell into bad company; for surely the good people are the worst of all company any one could come across.

It so happened that Billy was going home one clear frosty night not long after Christmas; the moon was round and bright; but although it was as fine a night as heart could wish for, he felt pinched with cold. 'By my word,' chattered Billy, 'a drop of good liquor would be no bad thing to keep a man's soul from freezing in him; and I wish I had a full measure of the best.'

'Never wish it twice, Billy,' said a little man in a three-cornered hat, bound all about with gold lace, and with great silver buckles in his shoes, so big that it was a wonder how he could carry them, and he held out a glass as big as himself, filled with as good liquor as ever eye looked on or lip tasted.

'Success, my little fellow,' said Billy Mac Daniel, nothing daunted, though well he knew the little man to belong to the *good people*; 'here's your health, anyway, and thank you kindly; no matter who pays for the

---

1 A festival held in honour of some patron saint.

MASTER AND MAN

drink'; and he took the glass and drained it to the very bottom without ever taking a second breath to it.

'Success,' said the little man; 'and you're heartily welcome, Billy; but don't think to cheat me as you have done others, – out with your purse and pay me like a gentleman.'

'Is it I pay you?' said Billy; 'could I not just take you up and put you in my pocket as easily as a blackberry?'

'Billy Mac Daniel,' said the little man, getting very angry, 'you shall be my servant for seven years and a day, and that is the way I will be paid; so make ready to follow me.'

When Billy heard this he began to be very sorry for having used such bold words towards the little man; and he felt himself, yet could not tell how, obliged to follow the little man the live-long night about the country, up and down, and over hedge and ditch, and through bog and brake, without any rest.

When morning began to dawn the little man turned round to him and said, 'You may now go home, Billy, but on your peril don't fail to meet me in the Fort-field tonight; or if you do it may be the worse for you in the long run. If I find you a good servant, you will find me an indulgent master.'

Home went Billy Mac Daniel; and though he was tired and weary enough, never a wink of sleep could he get for thinking of the little man; but he was afraid not to do his bidding, so up he got in the evening, and away he went to the Fort-field. He was not long there before the little man came towards him and said, 'Billy, I want to go a long journey tonight; so saddle one of my horses, and you may saddle another for yourself, as you are to go along with me, and may be tired after your walk last night.'

Billy thought this very considerate of his master, and thanked him accordingly: 'But,' said he, 'if I may be so bold, sir, I would ask which is the way to your stable, for never a thing do I see but the fort here, and the old thorn tree in the corner of the field, and the stream running at the bottom of the hill, with the bit of bog over against us.'

'Ask no questions, Billy,' said the little man, 'but go over to that bit of bog, and bring me two of the strongest rushes you can find.'

THE MAGICAL FOLK OF IRELAND

Billy did accordingly, wondering what the little man would be at; and he picked two of the stoutest rushes he could find, with a little bunch of brown blossom stuck at the side of each, and brought them back to his master.

'Get up, Billy,' said the little man, taking one of the rushes from him and striding across it.

'Where shall I get up, please your honour?' said Billy.

'Why, upon horseback, like me, to be sure,' said the little man.

'Is it after making a fool of me you'd be,' said Billy, 'bidding me get a horseback upon that bit of a rush? May be you want to persuade me that the rush I pulled but a while ago out of the bog over there is a horse?'

'Up! Up! and no words,' said the little man, looking very angry; 'the best horse you ever rode was but a fool to it.' So Billy, thinking all this was in joke, and fearing to vex his master, straddled across the rush. 'Borram! Borram! Borram!' cried the little man three times (which, in English, means to become great), and Billy did the same after him; presently the rushes swelled up into fine horses, and away they went full speed; but Billy, who had put the rush between his legs, without much minding how he did it, found himself sitting on horseback the wrong way, which was rather awkward, with his face to the horse's tail; and so quickly had his steed started off with him that he had no power to turn round, and there was therefore nothing for it but to hold on by the tail.

At last they came to their journey's end, and stopped at the gate of a fine house. 'Now, Billy,' said the little man, 'do as you see me do, and follow me close; but as you did not know your horse's head from his tail, mind that your own head does not spin round until you can't tell whether you are standing on it or on your heels: for remember that old liquor, though able to make a cat speak, can make a man dumb.'

The little man then said some queer kind of words, out of which Billy could make no meaning; but he contrived to say them after him for all that; and in they both went through the key-hole of the door, and through one key-hole after another, until they got into the wine-cellar, which was well stored with all kinds of wine.

MASTER AND MAN

The little man fell to drinking as hard as he could, and Billy, noway disliking the example, did the same. 'The best of masters are you, surely,' said Billy to him; 'no matter who is the next; and well pleased will I be with your service if you continue to give me plenty to drink.'

'I have made no bargain with you,' said the little man, 'and will make none; but up and follow me.' Away they went, through key-hole after key-hole; and each mounting upon the rush which he left at the hall door, scampered off, kicking the clouds before them like snow-balls, as soon as the words 'Borram, Borram, Borram' had passed their lips.

When they came back to the Fort-field the little man dismissed Billy, bidding him to be there the next night at the same hour. Thus did they go on, night after night, shaping their course one night here, and another night there; sometimes north, and sometimes east, and sometimes south, until there was not a gentleman's wine-cellar in all Ireland they had not visited, and could tell the flavour of every wine in it as well, ay, better than the butler himself.

One night when Billy Mac Daniel met the little man as usual in the Fort-field, and was going to the bog to fetch the horses for their journey, his master said to him, 'Billy, I shall want another horse tonight, for may be we may bring back more company than we take.' So Billy, who now knew better than to question any order given to him by his master, brought a third rush, much wondering who it might be that would travel back in their company, and whether he was about to have a fellow-servant. 'If I have,' thought Billy, 'he shall go and fetch the horses from the bog every night; for I don't see why I am not, every inch of me, as good a gentleman as my master.'

Well, away they went, Billy leading the third horse, and never stopped until they came to a snug farmer's house, in the county Limerick, close under the old castle of Carrigogunniel, that was built, they say, by the great Brian Boru. Within the house there was great carousing going forward, and the little man stopped outside for some time to listen; then turning round all of a sudden, said, 'Billy, I will be a thousand years old tomorrow!'

'God bless us, sir,' said Billy; 'will you?'

'Don't say these words again, Billy,' said the little old man, 'or you

81

THE MAGICAL FOLK OF IRELAND

will be my ruin for ever. Now Billy, as I will be a thousand years in the world tomorrow, I think it is full time for me to get married.'

'I think so too, without any kind of doubt at all,' said Billy, 'if ever you mean to marry.'

'And to that purpose,' said the little man, 'have I come all the way to Carrigogunniel; for in this house, this very night, is young Darby Riley going to be married to Bridget Rooney; and as she is a tall and comely girl, and has come of decent people, I think of marrying her myself, and taking her off with me.'

'And what will Darby Riley say to that?' said Billy.

'Silence!' said the little man, putting on a mighty severe look; 'I did not bring you here with me to ask questions'; and without holding further argument, he began saying the queer words which had the power of passing him through the key-hole as free as air, and which Billy thought himself mighty clever to be able to say after him.

In they both went; and for the better viewing the company, the little man perched himself up as nimbly as a cocksparrow upon one of the big beams which went across the house over all their heads, and Billy did the same upon another facing him; but not being much accustomed to roosting in such a place, his legs hung down as untidy as may be, and it was quite clear he had not taken pattern after the way in which the little man had bundled himself up together. If the little man had been a tailor all his life he could not have sat more contentedly upon his haunches.

There they were, both master and man, looking down upon the fun that was going forward; and under them were the priest and piper, and the father of Darby Riley, with Darby's two brothers and his uncle's son; and there were both the father and the mother of Bridget Rooney, and proud enough the old couple were that night of their daughter, as good right they had; and her four sisters, with bran new ribbons in their caps, and her three brothers all looking as clean and as clever as any three boys in Munster, and there were uncles and aunts, and gossips and cousins enough besides to make a full house of it; and plenty was there to eat and drink on the table for every one of them, if they had been double the number.

MASTER AND MAN

Now it happened, just as Mrs Rooney had helped his reverence to the first cut of the pig's head which was placed before her, beautifully bolstered up with white savoys, that the bride gave a sneeze, which made everyone at table start, but not a soul said, 'God bless us.' All thinking that the priest would have done so, as he ought if he had done his duty, no one wished to take the word out of his mouth, which, unfortunately, was preoccupied with pig's head and greens. And after a moment's pause the fun and merriment of the bridal feast went on without the pious benediction.

Of this circumstance both Billy and his master were no inattentive spectators from their exalted stations. 'Ha!' exclaimed the little man, throwing one leg from under him with a joyous flourish, and his eye twinkled with a strange light, whilst his eyebrows became elevated into the curvature of Gothic arches; 'Ha!' said he, leering down at the bride, and then up at Billy, 'I have half of her now, surely. Let her sneeze but twice more, and she is mine, in spite of priest, mass-book, and Darby Riley.'

Again the fair Bridget sneezed; but it was so gently, and she blushed so much, that few except the little man took, or seemed to take, any notice; and no one thought of saying 'God bless us.'

Billy all this time regarded the poor girl with a most rueful expression of countenance; for he could not help thinking what a terrible thing it was for a nice young girl of nineteen, with large blue eyes, transparent skin, and dimpled cheeks, suffused with health and joy, to be obliged to marry an ugly little bit of a man, who was a thousand years old, barring a day.

At this critical moment the bride gave a third sneeze, and Billy roared out with all his might, 'God save us!' Whether this exclamation resulted from his soliloquy, or from the mere force of habit, he never could tell exactly himself; but no sooner was it uttered than the little man, his face glowing with rage and disappointment, sprung from the beam on which he had perched himself, and shrieking out in the shrill voice of a cracked bagpipe, 'I discharge you from my service, Billy Mac Daniel – take that for your wages,' gave poor Billy a most furious kick in the back, which sent his unfortunate servant sprawling

THE MAGICAL FOLK OF IRELAND

upon his face and hands right in the middle of the supper-table.

If Billy was astonished, how much more so was every one of the company into which he was thrown with so little ceremony. But when they heard his story, Father Cooney laid down his knife and fork, and married the young couple out of hand with all speed; and Billy Mac Daniel danced the Rinka at their wedding, and plenty he did drink at it too, which was what he thought more of than dancing.

FAR DARRIG IN DONEGAL

Miss Letitia Maclintock

Pat Diver, the tinker, was a man well-accustomed to a wandering life, and to strange shelters; he had shared the beggar's blanket in smoky cabins; he had crouched beside the still in many a nook and corner where poteen was made on the wild Innishowen mountains; he had even slept on the bare heather, or on the ditch, with no roof over him but the vault of heaven; yet were all his nights of adventure tame and commonplace when compared with one especial night.

During the day preceding that night, he had mended all the kettles and saucepans in Moville and Greencastle, and was on his way to Culdaff, when night overtook him on a lonely mountain road.

He knocked at one door after another asking for a night's lodging, while he jingled the halfpence in his pocket, but was everywhere refused.

Where was the boasted hospitality of Innishowen, which he had never before known to fail? It was of no use to be able to pay when the people seemed so churlish. Thus thinking, he made his way towards a light a little further on, and knocked at another cabin door.

An old man and woman were seated one at each side of the fire.

'Will you be pleased to give me a night's lodging, sir?' asked Pat respectfully.

'Can you tell a story?' returned the old man.

'No, then, sir, I canna say I'm good at story-telling,' replied the puzzled tinker.

'Then you maun just gang further, for none but them that can tell a story will get in here.'

This reply was made in so decided a tone that Pat did not attempt to repeat his appeal, but turned away reluctantly to resume his weary journey.

'A story, indeed,' muttered he. 'Auld wives fables to please the weans!'

THE MAGICAL FOLK OF IRELAND

As he took up his bundle of tinkering implements, he observed a barn standing rather behind the dwelling-house, and, aided by the rising moon, he made his way towards it.

It was a clean, roomy barn, with a piled-up heap of straw in one corner. Here was a shelter not to be despised; so Pat crept under the straw, and was soon asleep.

He could not have slept very long when he was awakened by the tramp of feet, and, peeping cautiously through a crevice in his straw covering, he saw four immensely tall men enter the barn, dragging a body, which they threw roughly upon the floor.

They next lighted a fire in the middle of the barn, and fastened the corpse by the feet with a great rope to a beam in the roof. One of them then began to turn it slowly before the fire. 'Come on,' said he, addressing a gigantic fellow, the tallest of the four – 'I'm tired; you be to tak' your turn.'

'Faix an' troth, I'll no turn him,' replied the big man. 'There's Pat Diver in under the straw, why wouldn't he tak' his turn?'

With hideous clamour the four men called the wretched Pat, who, seeing there was no escape, thought it was his wisest plan to come forth as he was bidden.

'Now, Pat,' said they, 'you'll turn the corpse, but if you let him burn you'll be tied up there and roasted in his place.'

Pat's hair stood on end, and the cold perspiration poured from his forehead, but there was nothing for it but to perform his dreadful task.

Seeing him fairly embarked in it, the tall men went away.

Soon, however, the flames rose so high as to singe the rope, and the corpse fell with a great thud upon the fire, scattering the ashes and embers, and extracting a howl of anguish from the miserable cook, who rushed to the door, and ran for his life.

He ran on until he was ready to drop with fatigue, when, seeing a drain overgrown with tall, rank grass, he thought he would creep in there and lie hidden till morning.

But he was not many minutes in the drain before he heard the heavy tramping again, and the four men came up with their burthen, which they laid down on the edge of the drain.

FAR DARRIG IN DONEGAL

'I'm tired,' said one, to the giant; 'it's your turn to carry him a piece now.'

'Faix and troth, I'll no carry him,' replied he, 'but there's Pat Diver in the drain, why wouldn't he come out and tak' his turn?'

'Come out, Pat, come out,' roared all the men, and Pat, almost dead with fright, crept out.

He staggered on under the weight of the corpse until he reached Kiltown Abbey, a ruin festooned with ivy, where the brown owl hooted all night long, and the forgotten dead slept around the walls under dense, matted tangles of brambles and ben-weed.

No one ever buried there now, but Pat's tall companions turned into the wild graveyard, and began digging a grave.

Pat, seeing them thus engaged, thought he might once more try to escape, and climbed up into a hawthorn tree in the fence, hoping to be hidden in the boughs.

'I'm tired,' said the man who was digging the grave; 'here, take the spade,' addressing the big man, 'it's your turn.'

'Faix an' troth, it's no my turn,' replied he, as before. 'There's Pat Diver in the tree, why wouldn't he come down and tak' his turn?'

Pat came down to take the spade, but just then the cocks in the little farmyards and cabins round the abbey began to crow, and the men looked at one another.

'We must go,' said they, 'and well is it for you, Pat Diver, that the cocks crowed, for if they had not, you'd just ha' been bundled into that grave with the corpse.'

Two months passed, and Pat had wandered far and wide over the county Donegal, when he chanced to arrive at Raphoe during a fair.

Among the crowd that filled the Diamond he came suddenly on the big man.

'How are you, Pat Diver?' said he, bending down to look into the tinker's face.

'You've the advantage of me, sir, for I havna' the pleasure of knowing you,' faltered Pat.

'Do you not know me, Pat?' Whisper – 'When you go back to Innishowen, you'll have a story to tell!'

THE POOKA

The Pooka, *rectè* Púca, seems essentially an animal spirit. Some derive his name from *poc*, a he-goat; and speculative persons consider him the fore-father of Shakespere's 'Puck'. On solitary mountains and among old ruins he lives, 'grown monstrous with much solitude', and is of the race of the nightmare. 'In the MS. story, called 'Mac-na-Michomhairle', of uncertain authorship,' writes me Mr Douglas Hyde, 'we read that 'out of a certain hill in Leinster, there used to emerge as far as his middle, a plump, sleek, terrible steed, and speak in human voice to each person about November-day, and he was accustomed to give intelligent and proper answers to such as consulted him concerning all that would befall them until the November of next year. And the people used to leave gifts and presents at the hill until the coming of Patrick and the holy clergy.' This tradition appears to be a cognate one with that of the Púca.' Yes! unless it were merely an *augh-ishka* [*each-uisgé*] or Waterhorse. For these, we are told, were common once, and used to come out of the water to gallop on the sands and in the fields, and people would often go between them and the marge and bridle them, and they would make the finest of horses if only you could keep them away from sight of the water; but if once they saw a glimpse of the water, they would plunge in with their rider, and tear him to pieces at the bottom. It being a November spirit, however, tells in favour of the Pooka, for November-day is sacred to the Pooka. It is hard to realise that wild, staring phantom grown sleek and civil.

He has many shapes – is now a horse, now an ass, now a bull, now a goat, now an eagle. Like all spirits, he is only half in the world of form.

THE PIPER AND THE PUCA

Douglas Hyde

Translated literally from the Irish of the
Leabhar Sgeulaigheachta

In the old times, there was a half fool living in Dunmore, in the county Galway, and although he was excessively fond of music, he was unable to learn more than one tune, and that was the 'Black Rogue'. He used to get a good deal of money from the gentlemen, for they used to get sport out of him. One night the piper was coming home from a house where there had been a dance, and he half drunk. When he came to a little bridge that was up by his mother's house, he squeezed the pipes on, and began playing the 'Black Rogue' (*an rógaire dubh*). The Púca came behind him, and flung him up on his own back. There were long horns on the Púca, and the piper got a good grip of them, and then he said –

'Destruction on you, you nasty beast, let me home. I have a ten-penny piece in my pocket for my mother, and she wants snuff.'

'Never mind your mother,' said the Púca, ' but keep your hold. If you fall, you will break your neck and your pipes.' Then the Púca said to him, 'Play up for me the 'Shan Van Vocht' (*an t-seann-bhean bhocht*).'

'I don't know it,' said the piper.

'Never mind whether you do or you don't' said the Púca. 'Play up, and I'll make you know.'

The piper put wind in his bag, and he played such music as made himself wonder.

'Upon my word, you're a fine music-master,' says the piper then; 'but tell me where you're for bringing me.'

THE MAGICAL FOLK OF IRELAND

'There's a great feast in the house of the Banshee, on the top of Croagh Patric tonight,' says the Púca, 'and I'm for bringing you there to play music, and, take my word, you'll get the price of your trouble.'

'By my word, you'll save me a journey, then,' says the piper, 'for Father William put a journey to Croagh Patric on me, because I stole the white gander from him last Martinmas.'

The Púca rushed him across hills and bogs and rough places, till he brought him to the top of Croagh Patric. Then the Púca struck three blows with his foot, and a great door opened, and they passed in together, into a fine room.

The piper saw a golden table in the middle of the room, and hundreds of old women (*cailleacha*) sitting round about it. The old women rose up, and said, 'A hundred thousand welcomes to you, you Púca of November (*na Samhna*). Who is this you have with you?'

'The best piper in Ireland,' says the Púca.

One of the old women struck a blow on the ground, and a door opened in the side of the wall, and what should the piper see coming out but the white gander which he had stolen from Father William.

'By my conscience, then,' says the piper, 'myself and my mother ate every taste of that gander, only one wing, and I gave that to Moy-rua (Red Mary), and it's she told the priest I stole his gander.'

The gander cleaned the table, and carried it away, and the Púca said, 'Play up music for these ladies.'

The piper played up, and the old women began dancing, and they were dancing till they were tired. Then the Púca said to pay the piper, and every old woman drew out a gold piece, and gave it to him.

'By the tooth of Patric,' said he, 'I'm as rich as the son of a lord.'

'Come with me,' says the Púca, 'and I'll bring you home.'

They went out then, and just as he was going to ride on the Púca, the gander came up to him, and gave him a new set of pipes. The Púca was not long until he brought him to Dunmore, and he threw the piper off at the little bridge, and then he told him to go home, and says to him, 'You have two things now that you never had before – you have sense and music (*ciall agus ceól*).

The piper went home, and he knocked at his mother's door, saying,

THE PIPER AND THE PUCA

'Let me in, I'm as rich as a lord, and I'm the best piper in Ireland.'

'You're drunk,' said the mother.

'No, indeed,' says the piper, 'I haven't drunk a drop.'

The mother let him in, and he gave her the gold pieces, and, 'Wait now,' says he, 'till you hear the music I'll play.'

He buckled on the pipes, but instead of music, there came a sound as if all the geese and ganders in Ireland were screeching together. He wakened the neighbours, and they were all mocking him, until he put on the old pipes, and then he played melodious music for them; and after that he told them all he had gone through that night.

The next morning, when his mother went to look at the gold pieces, there was nothing there but the leaves of a plant.

The piper went to the priest, and told him his story, but the priest would not believe a word from him, until he put the pipes on him, and then the screeching of the ganders and geese began.

'Leave my sight, you thief,' says the priest.

But nothing would do the piper till he would put the old pipes on him to show the priest that his story was true.

He buckled on the old pipes, and he played melodious music, and from that day till the day of his death, there was never a piper in the county Galway was as good as he was.

DANIEL O'ROURKE

T. Crofton Croker

People may have heard of the renowned adventures of Daniel O'Rourke, but how few are there who know that the cause of all his perils, above and below, was neither more nor less than his having slept under the walls of the Pooka's tower. I knew the man well. He lived at the bottom of Hungry Hill, just at the right-hand side of the road as you go towards Bantry. An old man was he, at the time he told me the story, with grey hair and a red nose; and it was on the 25th of June 1813 that I heard it from his own lips, as he sat smoking his pipe under the old poplar tree, on as fine an evening as ever shone from the sky. I was going to visit the caves in Dursey Island, having spent the morning at Glengariff.

'I am often *axed* to tell it, sir,' said he, 'so that this is not the first time. The master's son, you see, had come from beyond foreign parts in France and Spain, as young gentlemen used to go before Buonaparte or any such was heard of; and sure enough there was a dinner given to all the people on the ground, gentle and simple, high and low, rich and poor. The *ould* gentlemen were the gentlemen after all, saving your honour's presence. They'd swear at a body a little, to be sure, and, may be, give one a cut of a whip now and then, but we were no losers by it in the end; and they were so easy and civil, and kept such rattling houses, and thousands of welcomes; and there was no grinding for rent, and there was hardly a tenant on the estate that did not taste of his landlord's bounty often and often in a year; but now it's another thing. No matter for that, sir, for I'd better be telling you my story.

'Well, we had everything of the best, and plenty of it; and we ate, and we drank, and we danced, and the young master by the same token danced with Peggy Barry, from the Bohereen – a lovely young couple

DANIEL O'ROURKE

they were, though they are both low enough now. To make a long story short, I got, as a body may say, the same thing as tipsy almost, for I can't remember ever at all, no ways, how it was I left the place; only I did leave it, that's certain. Well, I thought, for all that, in myself, I'd just step to Molly Cronohan's, the fairy woman, to speak a word about the bracket heifer that was bewitched; and so as I was crossing the stepping-stones of the ford of Ballyashenogh, and was looking up at the stars and blessing myself – for why? it was Lady-day – I missed my foot, and souse I fell into the water. "Death alive!" thought I, "I'll be drowned now!" However, I began swimming, swimming, swimming away for the dear life, till at last I got ashore, somehow or other, but never the one of me can tell how, upon a *dissolute* island.

'I wandered and wandered about there, without knowing where I wandered, until at last I got into a big bog. The moon was shining as bright as day, or your fair lady's eyes, sir (with your pardon for mentioning her), and I looked east and west, and north and south, and every way, and nothing did I see but bog, bog, bog – I could never find out how I got into it; and my heart grew cold with fear, for sure and certain I was that it would be my *berrin* place. So I sat down upon a stone which, as good luck would have it, was close by me, and I began to scratch my head, and sing the *Ullagone* – when all of a sudden the moon grew black, and I looked up, and saw something for all the world as if it was moving down between me and it, and I could not tell what it was. Down it came with a pounce, and looked at me full in the face; and what was it but an eagle? as fine a one as ever flew from the kingdom of Kerry. So he looked at me in the face, and says he to me, "Daniel O'Rourke," says he, "how do you do?" "Very well, I thank you, sir," says I; "I hope you're well"; wondering out of my senses all the time how an eagle came to speak like a Christian. "What brings you here, Dan," says he. "Nothing at all, sir," says I; "only I wish I was safe home again." "Is it out of the island you want to go, Dan?" says he. "'Tis, sir," says I: so I up and told him how I had taken a drop too much, and fell into the water; how I swam to the island; and how I got into the bog and did not know my way out of it. "Dan," says he, after a minute's thought, "though it is very improper for you to get

THE MAGICAL FOLK OF IRELAND

drunk on Lady-day, yet as you are a decent sober man, who 'tends mass well, and never fling stones at me or mine, nor cries out after us in the fields – my life for yours," says he; "so get up on my back, and grip me well for fear you'd fall off, and I'll fly you out of the bog." "I am afraid," says I, "your honour's making game of me; for who ever heard of riding a horseback on an eagle before?" "'Pon the honour of a gentleman," says he, putting his right foot on his breast, "I am quite in earnest: and so now either take my offer or starve in the bog – besides, I see that your weight is sinking the stone."

'It was true enough as he said, for I found the stone every minute going from under me. I had no choice; so thinks I to myself, faint heart never won fair lady, and this is fair persuadance. "I thank your honour," says I, "for the loan of your civility; and I'll take your kind offer." I therefore mounted upon the back of the eagle, and held him tight enough by the throat, and up he flew in the air like a lark. Little I knew the trick he was going to serve me. Up – up – up, God knows how far up he flew. "Why then," said I to him – thinking he did not know the right road home – very civilly, because why? I was in his power entirely; "sir," says I, "please your honour's glory, and with humble submission to your better judgment, if you'd fly down a bit, you're now just over my cabin, and I could be put down there, and many thanks to your worship."

"'*Arrah*, Dan," said he, "do you think me a, fool? Look down in the next field, and don't you see two men and a gun? By my word it would be no joke to be shot this way, to oblige a drunken blackguard that I picked up off of a *could* stone in a bog." "Bother you," said I to myself, but I did not speak out, for where was the use? Well, sir, up he kept, flying, flying, and I asking him every minute to fly down, and all to no use. "Where in the world are you going, sir?" says I to him. "Hold your tongue, Dan," says he: "mind your own business, and don't be interfering with the business of other people." "Faith, this is my business, I think," says I. "Be quiet, Dan," says he: so I said no more.

'At last where should we come to, but to the moon itself. Now you can't see it from this, but there is, or there was in my time, a reaping-

DANIEL O'ROURKE

hook sticking out of the side of the moon, this way (drawing the figure thus ◯ on the ground with the end of his stick).

"Dan," said the eagle, "I'm tired with this long fly; I had no notion 'twas so far." "And my lord, sir," said I, "who in the world axed you to fly so far – was it I? did not I beg and pray and beseech you to stop half an hour ago?" "There's no use talking, Dan," said he; "I'm tired bad enough, so you must get off, and sit down on the moon until I rest myself." "Is it sit down on the moon?" said I; "is it upon that little round thing, then? why, then, sure I'd fall off in a minute, and be *kilt* and spilt, and smashed all to bits; you are a vile deceiver – so you are." "Not at all, Dan," said he; "you can catch fast hold of the reaping-hook that's sticking out of the side of the moon, and 'twill keep you up." "I won't then," said I. "May be not," said he, quite quiet. "If you don't, my man, I shall just give you a shake, and one slap of my wing, and send you down to the ground, where every bone in your body will be smashed as small as a drop of dew on a cabbage-leaf in the morning." "Why, then, I'm in a fine way," said I to myself, "ever to have come along with the likes of you"; and so giving him a hearty curse in Irish, for fear he'd know what I said, I got off his back with a heavy heart, took hold of the reaping-hook, and sat down upon the moon, and a mighty cold seat it was, I can tell you that.

'When he had me there fairly landed, he turned about on me, and said, "Good morning to you, Daniel O'Rourke," said he; "I think I've nicked you fairly now. You robbed my nest last year" ('twas true enough for him, but how he found it out is hard to say), "and in return you are freely welcome to cool your heels dangling upon the moon like a cockthrow."

'"Is that all, and is this the way you leave me, you brute, you," says I. "You ugly unnatural baste, and is this the way you serve me at last? Bad luck to yourself, with your hook'd nose, and to all your breed, you blackguard." 'Twas all to no manner of use; he spread out his great big wings, burst out a laughing, and flew away like lightning. I bawled after him to stop; but I might have called and bawled for ever, without his minding me. Away he went, and I never saw him from that day to this – sorrow fly away with him! You may be sure I was in a

95

THE MAGICAL FOLK OF IRELAND

disconsolate condition, and kept roaring out for the bare grief, when all at once a door opened right in the middle of the moon, creaking on its hinges as if it had not been opened for a month before, I suppose they never thought of greasing 'em, and out there walks – who do you think, but the man in the moon himself? I knew him by his bush.

'"Good morrow to you, Daniel O'Rourke," said he; "how do you do?" "Very well, thank your honour," said I. "I hope your honour's well." "What brought you here, Dan?" said he. So I told him how I was a little overtaken in liquor at the master's, and how I was cast on a dissolute island, and how I lost my way in the bog, and how the thief of an eagle promised to fly me out of it, and how, instead of that, he had fled me up to the moon.

'"Dan," said the man in the moon, taking a pinch of snuff when I was done, "you must not stay here." "Indeed, sir," says I, "'tis much against my will I'm here at all; but how am I to go back?" "That's your business," said he; "Dan, mine is to tell you that here you must not stay; so be off in less than no time." "I'm doing no harm," says I, "only holding on hard by the reaping-hook, lest I fall off." "That's what you must not do, Dan," says he. "Pray, sir," says I, "may I ask how many you are in family, that you would not give a poor traveller lodging: I'm sure 'tis not so often you're troubled with strangers coming to see you, for 'tis a long way." "I'm by myself, Dan," says he; "but you'd better let go the reaping-hook." "Faith, and with your leave," says I, "I'll not let go the grip, and the more you bids me, the more I won't let go; – so I will." "You had better, Dan," says he again. "Why, then, my little fellow," says I, taking the whole weight of him with my eye from head to foot, "there are two words to that bargain; and I'll not budge, but you may if you like." "We'll see how that is to be," says he; and back he went, giving the door such a great bang after him (for it was plain he was huffed) that I thought the moon and all would fall down with it.

'Well, I was preparing myself to try strength with him, when back again he comes, with the kitchen cleaver in his hand, and, without saying a word, he gives two bangs to the handle of the reaping-hook that was keeping me up, and *whap*! it came in two. "Good morning

DANIEL O'ROURKE

to you, Dan," says the spiteful little old blackguard, when he saw me cleanly falling down with a bit of the handle in my hand; "I thank you for your visit, and fair weather after you, Daniel." I had not time to make any answer to him, for I was tumbling over and over, and rolling and rolling, at the rate of a fox-hunt. "God help me!" says I, "but this is a pretty pickle for a decent man to be seen in at this time of night: I am now sold fairly." The word was not out of my mouth when, whiz! what should fly by close to my ear but a flock of wild geese, all the way from my own bog of Ballyasheenogh, else how should they know *me*? The *ould* gander, who was their general, turning about his head, cried out to me, "Is that you, Dan?" "The same," said I, not a bit daunted now at what he said, for I was by this time used to all kinds of *bedevilment*, and, besides, I knew him of *ould*. "Good morrow to you," says he, "Daniel O'Rourke; how are you in health this morning?" "Very well, sir," says I, "I thank you kindly," drawing my breath, for I was mightily in want of some. "I hope your honour's the same." "I think 'tis falling you are, Daniel," says he. "You may say that, sir," says I. "And where are you going all the way so fast?" said the gander. So I told him how I had taken the drop, and how I came on the island, and how I lost my way in the bog, and how the thief of an eagle flew me up to the moon, and how the man in the moon turned me out. "Dan," said he, "I'll save you: put out your hand and catch me by the leg, and I'll fly you home." "Sweet is your hand in a pitcher of honey, my jewel," says I, though all the time I thought within myself that I don't much trust you; but there was no help, so I caught the gander by the leg, and away I and the other geese flew after him as fast as hops.

'We flew, and we flew, and we flew, until we came right over the wide ocean. I knew it well, for I saw Cape Clear to my right hand, sticking up out of the water. "Ah, my lord," said I to the goose, for I thought it best to keep a civil tongue in my head any way, "fly to land if you please." "It is impossible, you see, Dan," said he, "for a while, because you see we are going to Arabia." "To Arabia!" said I; "that's surely some place in foreign parts, far away. Oh! Mr Goose: why then, to be sure, I'm a man to be pitied among you." "Whist, whist, you fool," said he, "hold your tongue; I tell you Arabia is a very decent sort

THE MAGICAL FOLK OF IRELAND

of place, as like West Carbery as one egg is like another, only there is a little more sand there."

'Just as we were talking, a ship hove in sight, scudding so beautiful before the wind. "Ah! then, sir," said I, "will you drop me on the ship, if you please?" "We are not fair over it," said he; "if I dropped you now you would go splash into the sea." "I would not," says I; "I know better than that, for it is just clean under us, so let me drop now at once."

'"If you must, you must," said he; "there, take your own way;" and he opened his claw, and faith he was right – sure enough I came down plump into the very bottom of the salt sea! Down to the very bottom I went, and I gave myself up then for ever, when a whale walked up to me, scratching himself after his night's sleep, and looked me full in the face, and never the word did he say, but lifting up his tail, he splashed me all over again with the cold salt water till there wasn't a dry stitch upon my whole carcass! and I heard somebody saying – 'twas a voice I knew, too – "Get up, you drunken brute, off o' that"; and with that I woke up, and there was Judy with a tub full of water, which she was splashing all over me – for, rest her soul! though she was a good wife, she never could bear to see me in drink, and had a bitter hand of her own.

'"Get up," said she again: "and of all places in the parish would no place sarve your turn to lie down upon but under the *ould* walls of Carrigapooka? an uneasy resting I am sure you had of it." And sure enough I had: for I was fairly bothered out of my senses with eagles, and men of the moons, and flying ganders, and whales, driving me through bogs, and up to the moon, and down to the bottom of the green ocean. If I was in drink ten times over, long would it be before I'd lie down in the same spot again, I know that.'

THE KILDARE POOKA[1]

Patrick Kennedy

Mr H— R—, when he was alive, used to live a good deal in Dublin, and he was once a great while out of the country on account of the 'ninety-eight' business. But the servants kept on in the big house at Rath all the same as if the family was at home. Well, they used to be frightened out of their lives after going to their beds with the banging of the kitchen door, and the clattering of fire-irons, and the pots and plates and dishes. One evening they sat up ever so long, keeping one another in heart with telling stories about ghosts and fetches, and that when – what would you have of it? – the little scullery boy that used to be sleeping over the horses, and could not get room at the fire, crept into the hot hearth, and when he got tired listening to the stories, sorra fear him, but he fell dead asleep.

Well and good, after they were all gone and the kitchen fire raked up, he was woke with the noise of the kitchen door opening, and the trampling of an ass on the kitchen floor. He peeped out, and what should he see but a big ass, sure enough, sitting on his curabingo and yawning before the fire. After a little he looked about him, and began scratching his ears as if he was quite tired, and says he, 'I may as well begin first as last.' The poor boy's teeth began to chatter in his head, for says he, 'Now he's goin' to ate me'; but the fellow with the long ears and tail on him had something else to do. He stirred the fire, and then he brought in a pail of water from the pump, and filled a big pot that he put on the fire before he went out. He then put in his hand – foot, I mean – into the hot hearth, and pulled out the little boy. He let a roar

---

1 *Legendary Fictions of the Irish Celts* – Macmillan.

THE MAGICAL FOLK OF IRELAND

out of him with the fright, but the pooka only looked at him, and thrust out his lower lip to show how little he valued him, and then he pitched him into his pew again.

Well, he then lay down before the fire till he heard the boil coming on the water, and maybe there wasn't a plate, or a dish, or a spoon on the dresser that he didn't fetch and put into the pot, and wash and dry the whole bilin' of 'em as well as e'er a kitchen-maid from that to Dublin town. He then put all of them up on their places on the shelves; and if he didn't give a good sweepin' to the kitchen, leave it till again. Then he comes and sits fornent the boy, let down one of his ears, and cocked up the other, and gave a grin. The poor fellow strove to roar out, but not a dheeg 'ud come out of his throat. The last thing the pooka done was to rake up the fire, and walk out, giving such a slap o' the door, that the boy thought the house couldn't help tumbling down.

Well, to be sure if there wasn't a hullabullo next morning when the poor fellow told his story! They could talk of nothing else the whole day. One said one thing, another said another, but a fat, lazy scullery girl said the wittiest thing of all. ' Musha!' says she, 'if the pooka does be cleaning up everything that way when we are asleep, what should we be slaving ourselves for doing his work?' *'Shu gu dheine'*[2] says another; 'them's the wisest words you ever said, Kauth; it's meeself won't contradict you.'

So said, so done. Not a bit of a plate or dish saw a drop of water that evening, and not a besom was laid on the floor, and every one went to bed soon after sundown. Next morning everything was as fine as fine in the kitchen, and the lord mayor might eat his dinner off the flags. It was great ease to the lazy servants, you may depend, and everything went on well till a foolhardy gag of a boy said he would stay up one night and have a chat with the pooka.

He was a little daunted when the door was thrown open and the ass marched up to the fire.

'An then, sir,' says he, at last, picking up courage, 'if it isn't taking a

2 Meant for *seadh go deimhin* – i.e. yes, indeed.

THE KILDARE POOKA

liberty, might I ax who you are, and why you are so kind as to do half of the day's work for the girls every night?' 'No liberty at all,' says the pooka, says he: 'I'll tell you, and welcome. I was a servant in the time of Squire R.'s father, and was the laziest rogue that ever was clothed and fed, and done nothing for it. When my time came for the other world, this is the punishment was laid on me – to come here and do all this labour every night, and then go out in the cold. It isn't so bad in the fine weather; but if you only knew what it is to stand with your head between your legs, facing the storm, from midnight to sunrise, on a bleak winter night.' 'And could we do anything for your comfort, my poor fellow?' says the boy. 'Musha, I don't know,' says the pooka; 'but I think a good quilted frieze coat would help to keep the life in me them long nights.' 'Why then, in troth, we'd be the ungratefullest of people if we didn't feel for you.'

To make a long story short, the next night but two the boy was there again; and if he didn't delight the poor pooka, holding up a fine warm coat before him, it's no mather! Betune the pooka and the man, his legs was got into the four arms of it, and it was buttoned down the breast and the belly, and he was so pleased he walked up to the glass to see how he looked. 'Well,' says he, 'it's a long lane that has no turning. I am much obliged to you and your fellow-servants. You have made me happy at last. Goodnight to you.'

So he was walking out, but the other cried, 'Och! sure you're going too soon. What about the washing and sweeping?' 'Ah, you may tell the girls that they must now get their turn. My punishment was to last till I was thought worthy of a reward for the way I done my duty. You'll see me no more.' And no more they did, and right sorry they were for having been in such a hurry to reward the ungrateful pooka.

THE BANSHEE

The banshee (from *ban* [*bean*], a woman, and *shee* [*sidhe*] a fairy) is an attendant fairy that follows the old families, and none but them, and wails before a death. Many have seen her as she goes wailing and clapping her hands. The keen [*caoine*], the funeral cry of the peasantry, is said to be an imitation of her cry. When more than one banshee is present, and they wail and sing in chorus, it is for the death of some holy or great one. An omen that sometimes accompanies the banshee is the *coach-a-bower* [*cóiste-bodhar*] – an immense black coach, mounted by a coffin, and drawn by headless horses driven by a *Dullahan*. It will go rumbling to your door, and if you open it, according to Croker, a basin of blood will be thrown in your face. These headless phantoms are found elsewhere than in Ireland. In 1807 two of the sentries stationed outside St James's Park died of fright. A headless woman, the upper part of her body naked, used to pass at midnight and scale the railings. After a time the sentries were stationed no longer at the haunted spot. In Norway the heads of corpses were cut off to make their ghosts feeble. Thus came into existence the *Dullahans*, perhaps; unless, indeed, they are descended from that Irish giant who swam across the Channel with his head in his teeth. – Ed.

HOW THOMAS CONNOLLY MET THE BANSHEE

J. Todhunter

Aw, the banshee, sir? Well, sir, as I was striving to tell ye, I was going home from work one day, from Mr Cassidy's that I tould ye of, in the dusk o' the evening. I had more nor a mile – aye, it was nearer two mile – to thrack to, where I was ludgin' with a dacent widdy woman I knew, Biddy Maguire be name, so as to be near me work.

It was the first week in November, an' a lonesome road I had to travel, an' dark enough, wid threes above it; an' about half-ways there was a bit of a brudge I had to cross, over one o' them little sthrames that runs into the Doddher. I walked on in the middle iv the road, for there was no toe-path at that time, Misther Harry, nor for many a long day afther that; but, as I was sayin', I walked along till I come nigh upon the brudge, where the road was a bit open, an' there, right enough, I seen the hog's back o' the ould-fashioned brudge that used to be there till it was pulled down, an' a white mist steamin' up out o' the wather all around it.

Well, now, Misther Harry, often as I'd passed by the place before, that night it seemed sthrange to me, an' like a place ye might see in a dhrame; an' as I come up to it I began to feel a could wind blowin' through the hollow o' me heart. 'Musha Thomas,' sez I to meself, 'is it yerself that's in it?' sez I; 'or, if it is, what's the matter wid ye at all, at all?' sez I; so I put a bould face on it, an' I made a sthruggle to set one leg afore the other, ontil I came to the rise o' the brudge. And there, God be good to us! in a cantle o' the wall I seen an ould woman, as I thought, sittin' on her hunkers, all crouched together, an' her head bowed down, seemin'ly in the greatest affliction.

Well, sir, I pitied the ould craythur, an' thought I wasn't worth a thraneen, for the mortial fright I was in, I up an' sez to her, 'That's a cowld

THE MAGICAL FOLK OF IRELAND

lodgin' for ye, ma'am.' Well, the sorra ha'porth she sez to that, nor tuk no more notice o' me than if I hadn't let a word out o' me, but kep' rockin' herself to an' fro, as if her heart was breakin'; so I sez to her again, 'Eh, ma'am, is there anythin' the matther wid ye?' An' I made for to touch her on the shouldher, on'y some-thin' stopt me, for as I looked closer at her I saw she was no more an ould woman nor she was an ould cat. The first thing I tuk notice to, Misther Harry, was her hair, that was sthreelin' down over his showldhers, an' a good yard on the ground on aich side of her. O, be the hoky farmer, but that was the hair! The likes of it I never seen on mortial woman, young or ould, before nor sense. It grew as sthrong out of her as out of e'er a young slip of a girl ye could see; but the colour of it was a misthery to describe. The first squint I got of it I thought it was silvery grey, like an ould crone's; but when I got up beside her I saw, be the glance o' the sky, it was a soart iv an Iscariot colour, an' a shine out of it like floss silk. It ran over her showldhers and the two shapely arms she was lanin' her head on, for all the world like Mary Magdalen's in a picther; and then I persaved that the grey cloak and the green gownd undhernaith it was made of no earthly matarial I ever laid eyes on. Now, I needn't tell ye, sir, that I seen all this in the twinkle of a bed-post – long as I take to make the narration of it. So I made a step back from her, an' 'The Lord be betune us an' harm!' sez I, out loud, an' wid that I blessed meself. Well, Misther Harry, the word wasn't out o' me mouth afore she turned her face on me. Aw, Misther Harry, but 'twas that was the awfullest apparation ever I seen, the face of her as she looked up at me! God forgive me for sayin' it, but 'twas more like the face of the 'Axy Homo' beyand in Marlboro' Sthreet Chapel nor like any face I could mintion – as pale as a corpse, an' a most o' freckles on it, like the freckles on a turkey's egg; an' the two eyes sewn in wid red thread, from the terrible power o' crying the' had to do; an' such a pair iv eyes as the' wor, Misther Harry, as blue as two forget-me-nots, an' as cowld as the moon in a bog-hole of a frosty night, an' a dead-an'-live look in them that sent a cowld shiver through the marra o' me bones. Be the mortial! ye could ha' rung a tay cupful o' cowld paspiration out o' the hair o' me head that minute, so ye could. Well, I thought the life 'ud lave me intirely when she riz up from her hunkers, till, bedad! she looked mostly as tall as Nelson's Pillar; an' wid the two eyes gazin' back at me,

HOW THOMAS CONNOLLY MET THE BANSHEE

an' her two arms stretched out before hor, an' a keine out of her that riz the hair o' me scalp till it was as stiff as the hog's bristles in a new hearth broom, away she glides – glides round the angle o' the brudge, an' down with her into the sthrame that ran undhernaith it. 'Twas then I began to suspect what she was. 'Wisha, Thomas!' says I to meself, sez I; an' I made a great struggle to get me two legs into a throt, in spite o' the spavin o' fright the pair o' them wor in; an' how I brought meself home that same night the Lord in heaven only knows, for I never could tell; but I must ha' tumbled agin the door, and shot in head foremost into the middle o' the flure, where I lay in a dead swoon for mostly an hour; and the first I knew was Mrs Maguire stannin' over me with a jorum o' punch she was pourin' down me throath (throat), to bring back the life into me, an' me head in a pool of cowld wather she dashed over me in her first fright. 'Arrah, Mister Connolly,' shashee, 'what ails ye?' shashee, 'to put the scare on a lone woman like that?' shashee. 'Am I in this world or the next?' sez I. 'Musha! where else would ye be on'y here in my kitchen?' shashee. 'O, glory be to God!' sez I, 'but I thought I was in Purgathory at the laste, not to mintion an uglier place,' sez I, 'only it's too cowld I find meself, an' not too hot,' sez I. 'Faix, an' maybe ye wor more nor half-ways there, on'y for me,' shashee; 'but what's come to you at all, at all? Is it your fetch ye seen, Mister Connolly?' 'Aw, naboclish!'[1] sez I. 'Never mind what I seen,' sez I. So be degrees I began to come to a little; an' that's the way I met the banshee, Misther Harry !

'But how did you know it really was the banshee after all, Thomas?'

'Begor, sir, I knew the apparation of her well enough; but 'twas confirmed by a sarcumstance that occurred the same time. There was a Misther O'Nales was come on a visit, ye must know, to a place in the neighbourhood – one o' the ould O'Nales iv the county Tyrone, a rale ould Irish family – an' the banshee was heard keening round the house that same night, be more then one that was in it; an' sure enough, Misther Harry, he was found dead in his bed the next mornin'. So if it wasn't the banshee I seen that time, I'd like to know what else it could a' been.'

---

1 *Na bac leis* – i.e., don't mind it.

THE BANSHEE OF THE MAC CARTHYS

T. Crofton Croker

Charles Mac Carthy was, in the year 1749, the only surviving son of a very numerous family. His father died when he was little more than twenty, leaving him the Mac Carthy estate, not much encumbered, considering that it was an Irish one. Charles was gay, handsome, unfettered either by poverty, a father, or guardians, and therefore was not, at the age of one-and-twenty, a pattern of regularity and virtue. In plain terms, he was an exceedingly dissipated – I fear I may say debauched, young man. His companions were, as may be supposed, of the higher classes of the youth in his neighbourhood, and, in general, of those whose fortunes were larger than his own, whose dispositions to pleasure were, therefore, under still less restrictions, and in whose example he found at once an incentive and an apology for his irregularities. Besides, Ireland, a place to this day not very remarkable for the coolness and steadiness of its youth, was then one of the cheapest countries in the world in most of those articles which money supplies for the indulgence of the passions. The odious exciseman, – with his portentous book in one hand, his unrelenting pen held in the other, or stuck beneath his hat-band, and the ink-bottle ('black emblem of the informer') dangling from his waistcoat-button – went not then from ale-house to ale-house, denouncing all those patriotic dealers in spirits, who preferred selling whiskey, which had nothing to do with English laws (but to elude them), to retailing that poisonous liquor, which derived its name from the British 'Parliament' that compelled its circulation among a reluctant people. Or if the gauger – recording angel of the law – wrote dowm the peccadillo of a publican, he dropped a tear upon the word, and blotted it out for ever! For, welcome to the tables of their hospitable neighbours, the guardians

THE BANSHEE OF THE MAC CARTHYS

of the excise, where they existed at all, scrupled to abridge those luxuries which they freely shared; and thus the competition in the market between the smuggler, who incurred little hazard, and the personage ycleped fair trader, who enjoyed little protection, made Ireland a land flowing, not merely with milk and honey, but with whiskey and wine. In the enjoyments supplied by these, and in the many kindred pleasures to which frail youth is but too prone, Charles Mac Carthy indulged to such a degree, that just about the time when he had completed his four-and-twentieth year, after a week of great excesses, he was seized with a violent fever, which, from its malignity, and the weakness of his frame, left scarcely a hope of his recovery. His mother, who had at first made many efforts to check his vices, and at last had been obliged to look on at his rapid progress to ruin in silent despair, watched day and night at his pillow. The anguish of parental feeling was blended with that still deeper misery which those only know who have striven hard to rear in virtue and piety a beloved and favourite child; have found him grow up all that their hearts could desire, until he reached manhood; and then, when their pride was highest, and their hopes almost ended in the fulfilment of their fondest expectations, have seen this idol of their affections plunge headlong into a course of reckless profligacy, and, after a rapid career of vice, hang upon the verge of eternity, without the leisure or the power of repentance. Fervently she prayed that, if his life could not be spared, at least the delirium, which continued with increasing violence from the first few hours of his disorder, might vanish before death, and leave enough of light and of calm for making his peace with offended Heaven. After several days, however, nature seemed quite exhausted, and he sunk into a state too like death to be mistaken for the repose of sleep. His face had that pale, glossy, marble look, which is in general so sure a symptom that life has left its tenement of clay. His eyes were closed and sunk; the lids having that compressed and stiffened appearance which seemed to indicate that some friendly hand had done its last office. The lips, half closed and perfectly ashy, discovered just so much of the teeth as to give to the features of death their most ghastly, but most impressive look. He lay upon his back, with his hands stretched beside him, quite motionless; and his distracted mother, after repeated trials, could discover not the

THE MAGICAL FOLK OF IRELAND

least symptom of animation. The medical man who attended, having tried the usual modes for ascertaining the presence of life, declared at last his opinion that it was flown, and prepared to depart from the house of mourning. His horse was seen to come to the door. A crowd of people who were collected before the windows, or scattered in groups on the lawn in front, gathered around when the door opened. These were tenants, fosterers, and poor relations of the family, with others attracted by affection, or by that interest which partakes of curiosity, but is something more, and which collects the lower ranks round a house where a human being is in his passage to another world. They saw the professional man come out from the hall door and approach his horse; and while slowly, and with a melancholy air, he prepared to mount, they clustered round him with inquiring and wistful looks. Not a word was spoken, but their meaning could not be misunderstood; and the physician, when he had got into his saddle, and while the servant was still holding the bridle as if to delay him, and was looking anxiously at his face as if expecting that he would relieve the general suspense, shook his head, and said in a low voice, 'It's all over, James'; and moved slowly away. The moment he had spoken, the women present, who were very numerous, uttered a shrill cry, which, having been sustained for about half a minute, fell suddenly into a full, loud, continued, and discordant but plaintive wailing, above which occasionally were heard the deep sounds of a man's voice, sometimes in deep sobs, sometimes in more distinct exclamations of sorrow. This was Charles's foster-brother, who moved about the crowd, now clapping his hands, now rubbing them together in an agony of grief. The poor fellow had been Charles's playmate and companion when a boy, and afterwards his servant; had always been distinguished by his peculiar regard, and loved his young master as much, at least, as he did his own life.

When Mrs Mac Carthy became convinced that the blow was indeed struck, and that her beloved son was sent to his last account, even in the blossoms of his sin, she remained for some time gazing with fixedness upon his cold features; then, as if something had suddenly touched the string of her tenderest affections, tear after tear trickled down her cheeks, pale with anxiety and watching. Still she continued looking at her son, apparently unconscious that she was weeping, without once

108

THE BANSHEE OF THE MAC CARTHYS

lifting her handkerchief to her eyes, until reminded of the sad duties which the custom of the country imposed upon her, by the crowd of females belonging to the better class of the peasantry, who now, crying audibly, nearly filled the apartment. She then withdrew, to give directions for the ceremony of waking, and for supplying the numerous visitors of all ranks with the refreshments usual on these melancholy occasions. Though her voice was scarcely heard, and though no one saw her but the servants and one or two old followers of the family, who assisted her in the necessary arrangements, everything was conducted with the greatest regularity; and though she made no effort to check her sorrows they never once suspended her attention, now more than ever required to preserve order in her household, which, in this season of calamity, but for her would have been all confusion.

The night was pretty far advanced; the boisterous lamentations which had prevailed during part of the day in and about the house had given place to a solemn and mournful stillness; and Mrs Mac Carthy, whose heart, notwith-standing her long fatigue and watching, was yet too sore for sleep, was kneeling in fervent prayer in a chamber adjoining that of her son. Suddenly her devotions were disturbed by an unusual noise, proceeding from the persons who were watching round the body. First there was a low murmur, then all was silent, as if the movements of those in the chamber were checked by a sudden panic, and then a loud cry of terror burst from all within. The door of the chamber was thrown open, and all who were not overturned in the press rushed wildly into the passage which led to the stairs, and into which Mrs Mac Carthy's room opened. Mrs Mac Carthy made her way through the crowd into her son's chamber, where she found him sitting up in the bed, and looking vacantly around, like one risen from the grave. The glare thrown upon his sunk features and thin lathy frame gave an unearthly horror to his whole aspect Mrs Mac Carthy was a woman of some firmness; but she was a woman, and not quite free from the superstitions of her country. She dropped on her knees, and, clasping her hands, began to pray aloud. The form before her moved only its lips, and barely uttered 'Mother'; but though the pale lips moved, as if there was a design to finish the sentence, the tongue refused its office. Mrs Mac Carthy sprung forward,

THE MAGICAL FOLK OF IRELAND

and catching the arm of her son, exclaimed, 'Speak! in the name of God and His saints, speak! are you alive?'

He turned to her slowly, and said, speaking still with apparent difficulty, 'Yes, my mother, alive, and – but sit down and collect yourself; I have that to tell which will astonish you still more than what you have seen.' He leaned back upon his pillow, and while his mother remained kneeling by the bedside, holding one of his hands clasped in hers, and gazing on him with the look of one who distrusted all her senses, he proceeded: 'Do not interrupt me until I have done. I wish to speak while the excitement of returning life is upon me, as I know I shall soon need much repose. Of the commencement of my illness I have only a confused recollection; but within the last twelve hours I have been before the judgment-seat of God. Do not stare incredulously on me – 'tis as true as have been my crimes, and as, I trust, shall be repentance. I saw the awful Judge arrayed in all the terrors which invest him when mercy gives place to justice. The dreadful pomp of offended omnipotence, I saw – I remember. It is fixed here; printed on my brain in characters indelible; but it passeth human language. What I *can* describe I *will* – I may speak it briefly. It is enough to say, I was weighed in the balance, and found wanting. The irrevocable sentence was upon the point of being pronounced; the eye of my Almighty Judge, which had already glanced upon me, half spoke my doom; when I observed the guardian saint, to whom you so often directed my prayers when I was a child, looking at me with an expression of benevolence and compassion. I stretched forth my hands to him, and besought his intercession. I implored that one year, one month, might be given to me on earth to do penance and atonement for my transgressions. He threw himself at the feet of my Judge, and supplicated for mercy. Oh! never – not if I should pass through ten thousand successive states of being – never, for eternity, shall I forget the horrors of that moment, when my fate hung suspended – when an instant was to decide whether torments unutterable were to be my portion for endless ages! But Justice suspended its decree, and Mercy spoke in accents of firmness, but mildness, 'Return to that world in which thou hast lived but to outrage the laws of Him who made that world and thee. Three years are given thee for repentance; when these are ended, thou shalt again stand here, to be saved

THE BANSHEE OF THE MAC CARTHYS

or lost for ever.' I heard no more; I saw no more, until I awoke to life, the moment before you entered.'

Charles's strength continued just long enough to finish these last words, and on uttering them he closed his eyes, and lay quite exhausted. His mother, though, as was before said, somewhat disposed to give credit to supernatural visitations, yet hesitated whether or not she should believe that, although awakened from a swoon which might have been the crisis of his disease, he was still under the influence of delirium. Repose, however, was at all events necessary, and she took immediate measures that he should enjoy it undisturbed. After some hours' sleep, he awoke refreshed, and thenceforward gradually but steadily recovered.

Still he persisted in his account of the vision, as he had at first related it; and his persuasion of its reality had an obvious and decided influence on his habits and conduct. He did not altogether abandon the society of his former associates, for his temper was not soured by his reformation; but he never joined in their excesses, and often endeavoured to reclaim them. How his pious exertions succeeded, I have never learnt; but of himself it is recorded that he was religious without ostentation, and temperate without austerity; giving a practical proof that vice may be exchanged for virtue, without the loss of respectability, popularity, or happiness.

Time rolled on, and long before the three years were ended the story of his vision was forgotten, or, when spoken of, was usually mentioned as an instance proving the folly of believing in such things. Charles's health, from the temperance and regularity of his habits, became more robust than ever. His friends, indeed, had often occasion to rally him upon a seriousness and abstractedness of demeanour, which grew upon him as he approached the completion of his seven-and-twentieth year, but for the most part his manner exhibited the same animation and cheerfulness for which he had always been remarkable. In company he evaded every endeavour to draw from him a distinct opinion on the subject of the supposed prediction; but among his own family it was well known that he still firmly believed it. However, when the day had nearly arrived on which the prophecy was, if at all, to be fulfilled, his whole appearance gave such promise of a long and healthy life, that he

THE MAGICAL FOLK OF IRELAND

was persuaded by his friends to ask a large party to an entertainment at Spring House, to celebrate his birthday. But the occasion of this party, and the circumstances which attended it, will be best learned from a perusal of the following letters, which have been carefully preserved by some relations of his family. The first is from Mrs Mac Carthy to a lady, a very near connection and valued friend of her's, who lived in the county of Cork, at about fifty miles' distance from Spring House.

'To Mrs Barry, Castle Barry
'Spring House, Tuesday morning,
October 15th, 1752.

'My dearest Mary,

'I am afraid I am going to put your affection for your old friend and kinswoman to a severe trial. A two days' journey at this season, over bad roads and through a troubled country, it will indeed require friendship such as yours to persuade a sober woman to encounter. But the truth is, I have, or fancy I have, more than usual cause for wishing you near me. You know my son's story. I can't tell you how it is, but as next Sunday approaches, when the prediction of his dream, or vision, will be proved false or true, I feel a sickening of the heart, which I cannot suppress, but which your presence, my dear Mary, will soften, as it has done so many of my sorrows. My nephew, James Ryan, is to be married to Jane Osborne (who, you know, is my son's ward), and the bridal entertainment will take place here on Sunday next, though Charles pleaded hard to have it postponed for a day or two longer. Would to God – but no more of this till we meet. Do prevail upon yourself to leave your good man for one week, if his farming concerns will not admit of his accompanying you; and come to us, with the girls, as soon before Sunday as you can.

'Ever my dear Mary's attached cousin and friend,

'Ann Mac Carthy.'

THE BANSHEE OF THE MAC CARTHYS

Although this letter reached Castle Barry early on Wednesday, the messenger having travelled on foot over bog and moor, by paths impassable to horse or carriage, Mrs Barry, who at once determined on going, had so many arrangements to make for the regulation of her domestic affairs (which, in Ireland, among the middle orders of the gentry, fall soon into confusion when the mistress of the family is away), that she and her two young daughters were unable to leave until late on the morning of Friday. The eldest daughter remained to keep her father company, and superintend the concerns of the household. As the travellers were to journey in an open one-horse vehicle, called a jaunting-car (still used in Ireland), and as the roads, bad at all times, were rendered still worse by the heavy rains, it was their design to make two easy stages – to stop about midway the first night, and reach Spring House early on Saturday evening. This arrangement was now altered, as they found that from the lateness of their departure they could proceed, at the utmost, no farther than twenty miles on the first day; and they, therefore, purposed sleeping at the house of a Mr Bourke, a friend of theirs, who lived at somewhat less than that distance from Castle Barry. They reached Mr Bourke's in safety after a rather disagreeable ride. What befell them on their journey the next day to Spring House, and after their arrival there, is fully recounted in a letter from the second Miss Barry to her eldest sister.

'Spring House, Sunday evening,
20th October 1752.

'Dear Ellen,

'As my mother's letter, which encloses this, will announce to you briefly the sad intelligence which I shall here relate more fully, I think it better to go regularly through the recital of the extraordinary events of the last two days.

THE MAGICAL FOLK OF IRELAND

'The Bourkes kept us up so late on Friday night that yesterday was pretty far advanced before we could begin our journey, and the day closed when we were nearly fifteen miles distant from this place. The roads were excessively deep, from the heavy rains of the last week, and we proceeded so slowly that, at last, my mother resolved on passing the night at the house of Mr Bourke's brother (who lives about a quarter-of-a-mile off the road), and coming here to breakfast in the morning. The day had been windy and showery, and the sky looked fitful, gloomy, and uncertain. The moon was full, and at times shone clear and bright; at others it was wholly concealed behind the thick, black, and rugged masses of clouds that rolled rapidly along, and were every moment becoming larger, and collecting together as if gathering strength for a coming storm. The wind, which blew in our faces, whistled bleakly along the low hedges of the narrow road, on which we proceeded with difficulty from the number of deep sloughs, and which afforded not the least shelter, no plantation being within some miles of us. My mother, therefore, asked Leary, who drove the jaunting-car, how far we were from Mr Bourke's? "'Tis about ten spades from this to the cross, and we have then only to turn to the left into the avenue, ma'am." "Very well, Leary; turn up to Mr Bourke's as soon as you reach the cross roads." My mother had scarcely spoken these words, when a shriek, that made us thrill as if our very hearts were pierced by it, burst from the hedge to the right of our way. If it resembled anything earthly it seemed the cry of a female, struck by a sudden and mortal blow, and giving out her life in one long deep pang of expiring agony. "Heaven defend us!" exclaimed my mother. "Go you over the hedge, Leary, and save that woman, if she is not yet dead, while we run back to the hut we have just passed, and alarm the village near it." "Woman!" said Leary, beating the horse violently, while his voice trembled, "that's no woman; the sooner we get on, ma'am, the better'; and he continued his efforts to quicken the horse's pace. We saw nothing. The moon was hid. It was quite dark, and we had been for some time expecting a heavy fall of rain. But just as Leary had spoken, and had succeeded in making the horse trot briskly forward, we distinctly heard a loud clapping of

THE BANSHEE OF THE MAC CARTHYS

hands, followed by a succession of screams, that seemed to denote the last excess of despair and anguish, and to issue from a person running forward inside the hedge, to keep pace with our progress. Still we saw nothing; until, when we were within about ten yards of the place where an avenue branched off to Mr Bourke's to the left, and the road turned to Spring House on the right, the moon started suddenly from behind a cloud, and enabled us to see, as plainly as I now see this paper, the figure of a tall, thin woman, with uncovered head, and long hair that floated round her shoulders, attired in something which seemed either a loose white cloak or a sheet thrown hastily about her. She stood on the corner hedge, where the road on which we were met that which leads to Spring House, with her face towards us, her left hand pointing to this place, and her right arm waving rapidly and violently as if to draw us on in that direction. The horse had stopped, apparently frightened at the sudden presence of the figure, which stood in the manner I have described, still uttering the same piercing cries, for about half a minute. It then leaped upon the road, disappeared from our view for one instant, and the next was seen standing upon a high wall a little way up the avenue on which we purposed going, still pointing towards the road to Spring House, but in an attitude of defiance and command, as if prepared to oppose our passage up the avenue. The figure was now quite silent, and its garments, which had before flown loosely in the wind, were closely wrapped around it. "Go on, Leary, to Spring House, in God's name!" said my mother; "whatever world it belongs to, we will provoke it no longer." "'Tis the Banshee, ma'am," said Leary; "and I would not, for what my life is worth, go anywhere this blessed night but to Spring House. But I'm afraid there's something bad going forward, or she would not send us there." So saying, he drove forward; and as we turned on the road to the right, the moon suddenly withdrew its light, and we saw the apparition no more; but we heard plainly a prolonged clapping of hands, gradually dying away, as if it issued from a person rapidly retreating. We proceeded as quickly as the badness of the roads and the fatigue of the poor animal that drew us would allow, and arrived here about eleven o'clock last night. The scene which awaited us you have learned from my mother's letter. To explain it fully, I must recount to you some of the transactions which took place here during the last week.

'You are aware that Jane Osborne was to have been married this day to James Ryan, and that they and their friends have been here for the last week. On Tuesday last, the very day on the morning of which cousin Mac Carthy despatched the letter inviting us here, the whole of the company were walking about the grounds a little before dinner. It seems that an unfortunate creature, who had been seduced by James Ryan, was seen prowling in the neighbourhood in a moody, melancholy state for some days previous. He had separated from her for several months, and, they say, had provided for her rather handsomely; but she had been seduced by the promise of his marrying her; and the shame of her unhappy condition, uniting with disappointment and jealousy, had disordered her intellects. During the whole forenoon of this Tuesday she had been walking in the plantations near Spring House, with her cloak folded tight round her, the hood nearly covering her face; and she had avoided conversing with or even meeting any of the family.

'Charles Mac Carthy, at the time I mentioned, was walking between James Ryan and another, at a little distance from the rest, on a gravel path, skirting a shrubbery. The whole party was thrown into the utmost consternation by the report of a pistol, fired from a thickly planted part of the shrubbery which Charles and his companions had just passed. He fell instantly, and it was found that he had been wounded in the leg. One of the party was a medical man. His assistance was immediately given, and, on examining, he declared that the injury was very slight, that no bone was broken, it was merely a flesh wound, and that it would certainly be well in a few days. "We shall know more by Sunday," said Charles, as he was carried to his chamber. His wound was immediately dressed, and so slight was the inconvenience which it gave that several of his friends spent a portion of the evening in his apartment.

'On inquiry, it was found that the unlucky shot was fired by the poor girl I just mentioned. It was also manifest that she had aimed, not at

THE BANSHEE OF THE MAC CARTHYS

Charles, but at the destroyer of her innocence and happiness, who was walking beside him. After a fruitless search for her through the grounds, she walked into the house of her own accord, laughing and dancing, and singing wildly, and every moment exclaiming that she had at last killed Mr Ryan. When she heard that it was Charles, and not Mr Ryan, who was shot, she fell into a violent fit, out of which, after working convulsively for some time, she sprung to the door, escaped from the crowd that pursued her, and could never be taken until last night, when she was brought here, perfectly frantic, a little before our arrival.

'Charles's wound was thought of such little consequence that the preparations went forward, as usual, for the wedding entertainment on Sunday. But on Friday night he grew restless and feverish, and on Saturday (yesterday) morning felt so ill that it was deemed necessary to obtain additional medical advice. Two physicians and a surgeon met in consultation about twelve o'clock in the day, and the dreadful intelligence was announced, that unless a change, hardly hoped for, took place before night, death must happen within twenty-four hours after. The wound, it seems, had been too tightly bandaged, and otherwise injudiciously treated. The physicians were right in their anticipations. No favourable symptom appeared, and long before we reached Spring House every ray of hope had vanished. The scene we witnessed on our arrival would have wrung the heart of a demon. We heard briefly at the gate that Mr Charles was upon his death-bed. When we reached the house, the information was confirmed by the servant who opened the door. But just as we entered we were horrified by the most appalling screams issuing from the staircase. My mother thought she heard the voice of poor Mrs Mac Carthy, and sprung forward. We followed, and on ascending a few steps of the stairs, we found a young woman, in a state of frantic passion, struggling furiously with two men-servants, whose united strength was hardly sufficient to prevent her rushing upstairs over the body of Mrs Mac Carthy, who was lying in strong hysterics upon the steps. This, I afterwards discovered, was the unhappy girl I before described, who was attempting to gain access to Charles's room, to "get his forgiveness", as she said, "before he went

THE MAGICAL FOLK OF IRELAND

away to accuse her for having killed him". This wild idea was mingled with another, which seemed to dispute with the former possession of her mind. In one sentence she called on Charles to forgive her, in the next she would denounce James Ryan as the murderer, both of Charles and her. At length she was torn away; and the last words I heard her scream were, "James Ryan, 'twas you killed him, and not I – 'twas you killed him, and not I."

'Mrs Mac Carthy, on recovering, fell into the arms of my mother, whose presence seemed a great relief to her. She wept – the first tears, I was told, that she had shed since the fatal accident. She conducted us to Charles's room, who, she said, had desired to see us the moment of our arrival, as he found his end approaching, and wished to devote the last hours of his existence to uninterrupted prayer and meditation. We found him perfectly calm, resigned, and even cheerful. He spoke of the awful event which was at hand with courage and confidence, and treated it as a doom for which he had been preparing ever since his former remarkable illness, and which he never once doubted was truly foretold to him. He bade us farewell with the air of one who was about to travel a short and easy journey; and we left him with impressions which, notwithstanding all their anguish, will, I trust, never entirely forsake us.

'Poor Mrs Mac Carthy – but I am just called away. There seems a slight stir in the family; perhaps –'

The above letter was never finished. The enclosure to which it more than once alludes told the sequel briefly, and it is all that I have further learned of the family of Mac Carthy. Before the sun had gone down upon Charles's seven-and-twentieth birthday, his soul had gone to render its last account to its Creator.

GHOSTS

Ghosts, or as they are called in Irish, *Thevshi* or *Tash* (*taidhbhse, tais*),
live in a state intermediary between this life and the next. They are held
there by some earthly longing or affection, or some duty unfulfilled,
or anger against the living. 'I will haunt you,' is a common threat; and
one hears such phrases as, 'She will haunt him, if she has any good
in her.' If one is sorrowing greatly after a dead friend, a neighbour
will say, 'Be quiet now, you are keeping him from his rest'; or, in the
Western Isles, according to Lady Wilde, they will tell you, 'You are
waking the dog that watches to devour the souls of the dead.' Those
who die suddenly, more commonly than others, are believed to become
haunting Ghosts. They go about moving the furniture, and in every
way trying to attract attention.

When the soul has left the body, it is drawn away, sometimes, by the
fairies. I have a story of a peasant who once saw, sitting in a fairy rath,
all who had died for years in his village. Such souls are considered lost.
If a soul eludes the fairies, it may be snapped up by the evil spirits.
The weak souls of young children are in especial danger. When a very
young child dies, the western peasantry sprinkle the threshold with the
blood of a chicken, that the spirits may be drawn away to the blood. A
Ghost is compelled to obey the commands of the living. 'The stable-
boy up at Mrs G—'s there,' said an old countryman, 'met the master
going round the yards after he had been two days dead, and told him
to be away with him to the lighthouse, and haunt that; and there he is
far out to sea still, sir. Mrs G— was quite wild about it, and dismissed
the boy.' A very desolate lighthouse poor devil of a Ghost! Lady Wilde
considers it is only the spirits who are too bad for heaven, and too good

THE MAGICAL FOLK OF IRELAND

for hell, who are thus plagued. They are compelled to obey some one they have wronged.

The souls of the dead sometimes take the shapes of animals. There is a garden at Sligo where the gardener sees a previous owner in the shape of a rabbit. They will sometimes take the forms of insects, especially of butterflies. If you see one fluttering near a corpse, that is the soul, and is a sign of its having entered upon immortal happiness. The author of the *Parochial Survey of Ireland*, 1814, heard a woman say to a child who was chasing a butterfly, 'How do you know it is not the soul of your grandfather.' On November eve the dead are abroad, and dance with the fairies.

As in Scotland, the fetch is commonly believed in. If you see the double, or fetch, of a friend in the morning, no ill follows; if at night, he is about to die.

A DREAM

William Allingham

I heard the dogs howl in the moonlight night;
I went to the window to see the sight;
All the Dead that ever I knew
Going one by one and two by two.

On they pass'd, and on they pass'd;
Townsfellows all, from first to last;
Born in the moonlight of the lane,
Quenched in the heavy shadow again.

Schoolmates, marching as when we play'd
At soldiers once – but now more staid;
Those were the strangest sight to me
Who were drown'd, I knew, in the awful sea.

Straight and handsome folk; bent and weak, too;
Some that I loved, and gasp'd to speak to;
Some but a day in their churchyard bed;
Some that I had not known were dead.

A long, long crowd – where each seem'd lonely,
Yet of them all there was one, one only,
Raised a head or look'd my way.
She lingered a moment, – she might not stay.

How long since I saw that fair pale face!
Ah! Mother dear! might I only place

THE MAGICAL FOLK OF IRELAND

My head on thy breast, a moment to rest,
While thy hand on my tearful cheek were prest!

On, on, a moving bridge they made
Across the moon-stream, from shade to shade,
Young and old, women and men;
Many long-forgot, but remember'd then.

And first there came a bitter laughter;
A sound of tears the moment after;
And then a music so lofty and gay,
That every morning, day by day,
I strive to recall it if I may.

GRACE CONNOR

Miss Letitia Maclintock

Thady and Grace Connor lived on the borders of a large turf bog, in the parish of Clondevaddock, where they could hear the Atlantic surges thunder in upon the shore, and see the wild storms of winter sweep over the Muckish mountain, and his rugged neighbours. Even in summer the cabin by the bog was dull and dreary enough.

Thady Connor worked in the fields, and Grace made a livelihood as a pedlar, carrying a basket of remnants of cloth, calico, drugget and frieze about the country. The people rarely visited any large town, and found it convenient to buy from Grace, who was welcomed in many a lonely house, where a table was hastily cleared, that she might display her wares. Being considered a very honest woman, she was frequently entrusted with commissions to the shops in Letterkenny and Ramelton. As she set out towards home, her basket was generally laden with little gifts for her children.

'Grace, dear,' would one of the kind housewives say, 'here's a farrel[1] of oaten cake, wi' a taste o' butter on it; tak' it wi' you for the weans'; or, 'Here's half-a-dozen of eggs; you've a big family to support.'

Small Connors of all ages crowded round the weary mother, to rifle her basket of these gifts. But her thrifty, hard life came suddenly to an end. She died after an illness of a few hours, and was waked and buried as handsomely as Thady could afford.

Thady was in bed the night after the funeral, and the fire still burned brightly, when he saw his departed wife cross the room and bend over

---

1 When a large, round, flat griddle cake is divided into triangular cuts, each of these cuts is called a farrel, farli, or parli.

THE MAGICAL FOLK OF IRELAND

the cradle. Terrified, he muttered rapid prayers, covered his face with the blanket; and on looking up again the appearance was gone.

Next night he lifted the infant out of the cradle, and laid it behind him in the bed, hoping thus to escape his ghostly visitor; but Grace was presently in the room, and stretching over him to wrap up her child. Shrinking and shuddering, the poor man exclaimed, 'Grace, woman, what is it brings you back? What is it you want wi' me?'

'I want naething fae you, Thady, but to put thon wean back in her cradle,' replied the spectre, in a tone of scorn. 'You're too feared for me, but my sister Rose willna be feared for me – tell her to meet me tomorrow evening, in the old wallsteads.'

Rose lived with her mother, about a mile off, but she obeyed her sister's summons without the least fear, and kept the strange tryste in due time.

'Rose, dear,' she said, as she appeared before her sister in the old wallsteads, 'my mind's oneasy about them twa' red shawls that's in the basket. Matty Hunter and Jane Taggart paid me for them, an' I bought them wi' their money, Friday was eight days. Gie them the shawls the morrow. An' old Mosey McCorkell gied me the price o' a wiley coat; it's in under the other things in the basket. An' now farewell; I can get to my rest.'

'Grace, Grace, bide a wee minute,' cried the faithful sister, as the dear voice grew fainter, and the dear face began to fade – 'Grace, darling! Thady? The children? One word mair!' but neither cries nor tears could further detain the spirit hastening to its rest!

THE RADIANT BOY

Mrs Crow

Captain Stewart, afterwards Lord Castlereagh, when he was a young man, happened to be quartered in Ireland. He was fond of sport, and one day the pursuit of game carried him so far that he lost his way. The weather, too, had become very rough, and in this strait he presented himself at the door of a gentleman's house, and sending in his card, requested shelter for the night. The hospitality of the Irish country gentry is proverbial; the master of the house received him warmly; said he feared he could not make him so comfortable as he could have wished, his house being full of visitors already, added to which, some strangers, driven by the inclemency of the night, had sought shelter before him, but such accommodation as he could give he was heartily welcome to; whereupon he called his butler, and committing the guest to his good offices, told him he must put him up somewhere, and do the best he could for him. There was no lady, the gentleman being a widower.

Captain Stewart found the house crammed, and a very jolly party it was. His host invited him to stay, and promised him good shooting if he would prolong his visit a few days: and, in fine, he thought himself extremely fortunate to have fallen into such pleasant quarters.

At length, after an agreeable evening, they all retired to bed, and the butler conducted him to a large room, almost divested of furniture, but with a blazing turf fire in the grate, and a shake-down on the floor, composed of cloaks and other heterogeneous materials.

Nevertheless, to the tired limbs of Captain Stewart, who had had a hard day's shooting, it looked very inviting; but before he lay down, he thought it advisable to take off some of the fire, which was blazing up the chimney in what he thought an alarming manner. Having done this, he stretched himself on his couch and soon fell asleep.

THE MAGICAL FOLK OF IRELAND

He believed he had slept about a couple of hours when he awoke suddenly, and was startled by such a vivid light in the room that he thought it on fire, but on turning to look at the grate he saw the fire was out, though it was from the chimney the light proceeded. He sat up in bed, trying to discover what it was, when he perceived the form of a beautiful naked boy, surrounded by a dazzling radiance. The boy looked at him earnestly, and then the vision faded, and all was dark. Captain Stewart, so far from supposing what he had seen to be of a spiritual nature, had no doubt that the host, or the visitors, had been trying to frighten him. Accordingly, he felt indignant at the liberty, and on the following morning, when he appeared at breakfast, he took care to evince his displeasure by the reserve of his demeanour, and by announcing his intention to depart immediately. The host expostulated, reminding him of his promise to stay and shoot. Captain Stewart coldly excused himself, and, at length, the gentleman seeing something was wrong, took him aside, and pressed for an explanation; whereupon Captain Stewart, without entering into particulars, said he had been made the victim of a sort of practical joking that he thought quite unwarrantable with a stranger.

The gentleman considered this not impossible amongst a parcel of thoughtless young men, and appealed to them to make an apology; but one and all, on honour, denied the impeachment. Suddenly a thought seemed to strike him; he clapt his hand to his forehead, uttered an exclamation, and rang the bell.

'Hamilton,' said he to the butler; 'where did Captain Stewart sleep last night?'

'Well, sir,' replied the man; 'you know every place was full – the gentlemen were lying on the floor, three or four in a room – so I gave him the *Boy's Room*; but I lit a blazing fire to keep him from coming out.'

'You were very wrong,' said the host; 'you know I have positively forbidden you to put anyone there, and have taken the furniture out of the room to ensure its not being occupied.' Then, retiring with Captain Stewart, he informed him, very gravely, of the nature of the phenomena he had seen; and at length, being pressed for further information, he

THE RADIANT BOY

confessed that there existed a tradition in the family, that whoever the 'Radiant boy' appeared to will rise to the summit of power; and when he has reached the climax, will die a violent death, and I must say, he added, that the records that have been kept of his appearance go to confirm this persuasion.

THE FATE OF FRANK M'KENNA

William Carleton

There lived a man named M'Kenna at the hip of one of the mountainous hills which divide the county of Tyrone from that of Monaghan. This M'Kenna had two sons, one of whom was in the habit of tracing hares of a Sunday whenever there happened to be a fall of snow. His father, it seems, had frequently remonstrated with him upon what he considered to be a violation of the Lord's day, as well as for his general neglect of mass. The young man, however, though otherwise harmless and inoffensive, was in this matter quite insensible to paternal reproof, and continued to trace whenever the avocations of labour would allow him. It so happened that upon a Christmas morning, I think in the year 1814, there was a deep fall of snow, and young M'Kenna, instead of going to mass, got down his cock-stick – which is a staff much thicker and heavier at one end than at the other – and prepared to set out on his favourite amusement. His father, seeing this, reproved him seriously, and insisted that he should attend prayers. His enthusiasm for the sport, however, was stronger than his love of religion, and he refused to be guided by his father's advice. The old man during the altercation got warm; and on finding that the son obstinately scorned his authority, he knelt down and prayed that if the boy persisted in following his own will, he might never return from the mountains unless as a corpse. The imprecation, which was certainly as harsh as it was impious and senseless, might have startled many a mind from a purpose that was, to say the least of it, at variance with religion and the respect due to a father. It had no effect, however, upon the son, who is said to have replied, that whether he ever returned or not, he was determined on going; and go accordingly he did. He was not, however, alone, for it appears that three or four of the neighbouring young men accompanied

THE FATE OF FRANK M'KENNA

him. Whether their sport was good or otherwise, is not to the purpose, neither am I able to say; but the story goes that towards the latter part of the day they started a larger and darker hare than any they had ever seen, and that she kept dodging on before them bit by bit, leading them to suppose that every succeeding cast of the cock-stick would bring her down. It was observed afterwards that she also led them into the recesses of the mountains, and that although they tried to turn her course homewards, they could not succeed in doing so. As evening advanced, the companions of M'Kenna began to feel the folly of pursuing her farther, and to perceive the danger of losing their way in the mountains should night or a snow-storm come upon them. They therefore proposed to give over the chase and return home; but M'Kenna would not hear of it. 'If you wish to go home, you may,' said he; 'as for me, I'll never leave the hills till I have her with me.' They begged and entreated of him to desist and return, but all to no purpose: he appeared to be what the Scotch call *fey* – that is, to act as if he were moved by some impulse that leads to death, and from the influence of which a man cannot withdraw himself. At length, on finding him invincibly obstinate, they left him pursuing the hare directly into the heart of the mountains, and returned to their respective homes.

In the meantime one of the most terrible snow-storms ever remembered in that part of the country came on, and the consequence was, that the self-willed young man, who had equally trampled on the sanctities of religion and parental authority, was given over for lost. As soon as the tempest became still, the neighbours assembled in a body and proceeded to look for him. The snow, however, had fallen so heavily that not a single mark of a footstep could be seen. Nothing but one wide waste of white undulating hills met the eye wherever it turned, and of M'Kenna no trace whatever was visible or could be found. His father, now remembering the unnatural character of his imprecation, was nearly distracted; for although the body had not yet been found, still by every one who witnessed the sudden rage of the storm and who knew the mountains, escape or survival was felt to be impossible. Every day for about a week large parties were out among the hill-ranges seeking him, but to no purpose. At length there came a thaw,

THE MAGICAL FOLK OF IRELAND

and his body was found on a snow-wreath, lying in a supine posture within a circle which he had drawn around him with his cock-stick. His prayer-book lay opened upon his mouth, and his hat was pulled down so as to cover it and his face. It is unnecessary to say that the rumour of his death, and of the circumstances under which he left home, created a most extraordinary sensation in the country – a sensation that was the greater in proportion to the uncertainty occasioned by his not having been found either alive or dead. Some affirmed that he had crossed the mountains, and was seen in Monaghan; others, that he had been seen in Clones, in Emyvale, in Five-mile-town; but despite of all these agreeable reports, the melancholy truth was at length made clear by the appearance of the body as just stated.

Now, it so happened that the house nearest the spot where he lay was inhabited by a man named Daly, I think – but of the name I am not certain – who was a herd or care-taker to Dr Porter, then Bishop of Clogher. The situation of this house was the most lonely and desolate-looking that could be imagined. It was at least two miles distant from any human habitation, being surrounded by one wide and dreary waste of dark moor. By this house lay the route of those who had found the corpse, and I believe the door of it was borrowed for the purpose of conveying it home. Be this as it may, the family witnessed the melancholy procession as it passed slowly through the mountains, and when the place and circumstances are all considered, we may admit that to ignorant and superstitious people, whose minds, even upon ordinary occasions, were strongly affected by such matters, it was a sight calculated to leave, behind it a deep, if not a terrible impression. Time soon proved that it did so.

An incident is said to have occurred at the funeral in fine keeping with the wild spirit of the whole melancholy event. When the procession had advanced to a place called Mullaghtinny, a large dark-coloured hare, which was instantly recognised, by those who had been out with him on the hills, as the identical one that led him to his fate, is said to have crossed the roads about twenty yards or so before the coffin. The story goes, that a man struck it on the side with a stone, and that the blow, which would have killed any ordinary hare, not only did it no

130

THE FATE OF FRANK M'KENNA

injury, but occasioned a sound to proceed from the body resembling the hollow one emitted by an empty barrel when struck.

In the meantime the interment took place, and the sensation began, like every other, to die away in the natural progress of time, when, behold, a report ran abroad like wild-fire that, to use the language of the people, 'Frank M'Kenna was *appearing!*'

One night, about a fortnight after his funeral, the daughter of Daly, the herd, a girl about fourteen, while lying in bed saw what appeared to be the likeness of M'Kenna, who had been lost. She screamed out, and covering her head with the bed-clothes, told her father and mother that Frank M'Kenna was in the house. This alarming intelligence naturally produced great terror; still, Daly, who, notwithstanding his belief in such matters, possessed a good deal of moral courage, was cool enough to rise and examine the house, which consisted of only one apartment. This gave the daughter some courage, who, on finding that her father could not see him, ventured to look out, and she *then* could see nothing of him herself. She very soon fell asleep, and her father attributed what she saw to fear, or some accidental combination of shadows proceeding from the furniture, for it was a clear moonlight night. The light of the following day dispelled a great deal of their apprehensions, and comparatively little was thought of it until evening again advanced, when the fears of the daughter began to return. They appeared to be prophetic, for she said when night came that she knew he would appear again; and accordingly at the same hour he did so. This was repeated for several successive nights, until the girl, from the very hardihood of terror, began to become so far familiarised to the spectre as to venture to address it.

'In the name of God!' she asked, 'what is troubling you, or why do you appear to me instead of to some of your own family or relations?'

The ghost's answer alone might settle the question involved in the authenticity of its appearance, being, as it was, an account of one of the most ludicrous missions that ever a spirit was despatched upon.

'I'm not allowed,' said he, 'to spake to any of my friends, for I parted wid them in anger; but I'm come to tell you that they are quarrelin' about my breeches – a new pair that I got made for Christmas day; an'

THE MAGICAL FOLK OF IRELAND

as I was comin' up to thrace in the mountains, I thought the ould one 'ud do betther, a' of coorse I didn't put the new pair an me. My raison for appearin',' he added, 'is, that you may tell my friends that none of them is to wear them – they must be given in charity.'

This serious and solemn intimation from the ghost was duly communicated to the family, and it was found that the circumstances were exactly as it had represented them. This, of course, was considered as sufficient proof of the truth of its mission. Their conversations now became not only frequent, but quite friendly and familiar. The girl became a favourite with the spectre, and the spectre, on the other hand, soon lost all his terrors in her eyes. He told her that whilst his friends were bearing home his body, the handspikes or poles on which they carried him had cut his back, and *occasioned him great pain*! The cutting of the back also was known to be true, and strengthened, of course, the truth and authenticity of their dialogues. The whole neighbourhood was now in a commotion with this story of the apparition, and persons incited by curiosity began to visit the girl in order to satisfy themselves of the truth of what they had heard. Everything, however, was corroborated, and the child herself, without any symptoms of anxiety or terror, artlessly related her conversations with the spirit. Hitherto their interviews had been all nocturnal, but now that the ghost found his footing made good, he put a hardy face on, and ventured to appear by daylight. The girl also fell into states of syncope, and while the fits lasted, long conversations with him upon the subject of God, the blessed Virgin, and Heaven, took place between them. He was certainly an excellent moralist, and gave the best advice. Swearing, drunkenness, theft, and every evil propensity of our nature, were declaimed against with a degree of spectral eloquence quite surprising. Common fame had now a topic dear to her heart, and never was a ghost made more of by his best friends than she made of him. The whole country was in a tumult, and I well remember the crowds which flocked to the lonely little cabin in the mountains, now the scene of matters so interesting and important. Not a single day passed in which I should think from ten to twenty, thirty, or fifty persons, were not present at these singular interviews. Nothing else was talked of,

THE FATE OF FRANK M'KENNA

thought of, and, as I can well testify, dreamt of. I would myself have gone to Daly's were it not for a confounded misgiving I had, that perhaps the ghost might take such a fancy of appearing to *me*, as he had taken to cultivate an intimacy with the girl; and it so happens, that when I see the face of an individual nailed down in the coffin – chilling and gloomy operation! – I experience no particular wish to look upon it again.

The spot where the body of M'Kenna was found is now marked by a little heap of stones, which has been collected since the melancholy event of his death. Every person who passes it throws a stone upon the heap; but why this old custom is practised, or what it means, I do not know, unless it be simply to mark the spot as a visible means of preserving the memory of the occurrence.

Daly's house, the scene of the supposed apparition, is now a shapeless ruin, which could scarcely be seen were it not for the green spot that once was a garden, and which now shines at a distance like an emerald, but with no agreeable or pleasing associations. It is a spot which no solitary schoolboy will ever visit, nor indeed would the unflinching believer in the popular nonsense of ghosts wish to pass it without a companion. It is, under any circumstances, a gloomy and barren place; but when looked upon in connection with what we have just recited, it is lonely, desolate, and awful.

WITCHES, FAIRY DOCTORS

Witches and fairy doctors receive their power from opposite dynasties; the witch from evil spirits and her own malignant will; the fairy doctor from the fairies, and a something – a temperament – that is born with him or her. The first is always feared and hated. The second is gone to for advice, and is never worse than mischievous. The most celebrated fairy doctors are sometimes people the fairies loved and carried away, and kept with them for seven years; not that those the fairies love are always carried off – they may merely grow silent and strange, and take to lonely wanderings in the 'gentle' places. Such will, in after-times, be great poets or musicians, or fairy doctors; they must not be confused with those who have a *Lianhaun shee* [*leannán-sidhe*], for the *Lianhaun shee* lives upon the vitals of its chosen, and they waste and die. She is of the dreadful solitary fairies. To her have belonged the greatest of the Irish poets, from Oisin down to the last century.

Those we speak of have for their friends the trooping fairies – the gay and sociable populace of raths and caves. Great is their knowledge of herbs and spells. These doctors, when the butter will not come on the milk, or the milk will not come from the cow, will be sent for to find out if the cause be in the course of common nature or if there has been witchcraft. Perhaps some old hag in the shape of a hare has been milking the cattle. Perhaps some user of 'the dead hand' has drawn away the butter to her own churn. Whatever it be, there is the counter-charm. They will give advice, too, in cases of suspected changelings, and prescribe for the 'fairy blast' (when the fairy strikes any one a

WITCHES, FAIRY DOCTORS

tumour rises, or they become paralysed. This is called a 'fairy blast' or a 'fairy stroke'). The fairies are, of course, visible to them, and many a new-built house have they bid the owner pull down because it lay on the fairies' road. Lady Wilde thus describes one who lived in Innis Sark: – 'He never touched beer, spirits, or meat in all his life, but has lived entirely on bread, fruit, and vegetables. A man who knew him thus describes him – "Winter and summer his dress is the same – merely a flannel shirt and coat. He will pay his share at a feast, but neither eats nor drinks of the food and drink set before him. He speaks no English, and never could be made to learn the English tongue, though he says it might be used with great effect to curse one's enemy. He holds a burial-ground sacred, and would not carry away so much as a leaf of ivy from a grave. And he maintains that the people are right to keep to their ancient usages, such as never to dig a grave on a Monday, and to carry the coffin three times round the grave, following the course of the sun, for then the dead rest in peace. Like the people, also, he holds suicides as accursed; for they believe that all its dead turn over on their faces if a suicide is laid amongst them.

"'Though well off, he never, even in his youth, thought of taking a wife; nor was he ever known to love a woman. He stands quite apart from life, and by this means holds his power over the mysteries. No money will tempt him to impart his knowledge to another, for if he did he would be struck dead – so he believes. He would not touch a hazel stick, but carries an ash wand, which he holds in his hand when he prays, laid across his knees; and the whole of his life is devoted to works of grace and charity, and though now an old man, he has never had a day's sickness. No one has ever seen him in a rage, nor heard an angry word from his lips but once, and then being under great irritation, he recited the Lord's Prayer backwards as an imprecation on his enemy. Before his death he will reveal the mystery of his power, but not till the hand of death is on him for certain."' When he does reveal it, we may be sure it will be to one person only – his successor. There are several such doctors in County Sligo, really well up in herbal medicine by all accounts, and my friends find them in their own counties. All these things go on merrily. The spirit of the age

THE MAGICAL FOLK OF IRELAND

laughs in vain, and is itself only a ripple to pass, or already passing, away.

The spells of the witch are altogether different; they smell of the grave. One of the most powerful is the charm of the dead hand. With a hand cut from a corpse they, muttering words of power, will stir a well and skim from its surface a neighbour's butter.

A candle held between the fingers of the dead hand can never be blown out. This is useful to robbers, but they appeal for the suffrage of the lovers likewise, for they can make love-potions by drying and grinding into powder the liver of a black cat. Mixed with tea, and poured from a black teapot, it is infallible. There are many stories of its success in quite recent years, but, unhappily, the spell must be continually renewed, or all the lore may turn into hate. But the central notion of witchcraft everywhere is the power to change into some fictitious form, usually in Ireland a hare or a cat. Long ago a wolf was the favourite. Before Giraldus Cambrensis came to Ireland, a monk wandering in a forest at night came upon two wolves, one of whom was dying. The other entreated him to give the dying wolf the last sacrament. He said the mass, and paused when he came to the viaticum. The other, on seeing this, tore the skin from the breast of the dying wolf, laying bare the form of an old woman. Thereon the monk gave the sacrament.

Years afterwards he confessed the matter, and when Giraldus visited the country, was being tried by the synod of the bishops. To give the sacrament to an animal was a great sin. Was it a human being or an animal? On the advice of Giraldus they sent the monk, with papers describing the matter, to the Pope for his decision. The result is not stated.

Giraldus himself was of opinion that the wolf-form was an illusion, for, as he argued, only God can change the form. His opinion coincides with tradition, Irish and otherwise.

It is the notion of many who have written about these things that magic is mainly the making of such illusions. Patrick Kennedy tells a story of a girl who, having in her hand a sod of grass containing, unknown to herself, a four-leaved shamrock, watched a conjurer

WITCHES, FAIRY DOCTORS

at a fair. Now, the four-leaved shamrock guards its owner from all *pishogues* (spells), and when the others were staring at a cock carrying along the roof of a shed a huge beam in its bill, she asked them what they found to wonder at in a cock with a straw. The conjurer begged from her the sod of grass, to give to his horse, he said. Immediately she cried out in terror that the beam would fall and kill somebody.

This, then, is to be remembered – the form of an enchanted thing is a fiction and a caprice.

137

BEWITCHED BUTTER (DONEGAL)

Miss Letitia Maclintock

Not far from Rathmullen lived, last spring, a family called Hanlon; and in a farm-house, some fields distant, people named Dogherty. Both families had good cows, but the Hanlons were fortunate in possessing a Kerry cow that gave more milk and yellower butter that the others.

Grace Dogherty, a young girl, who was more admired than loved in the neighbourhood, took much interest in the Kerry cow, and appeared one night at Mrs Hanlon's door with the modest request –

'Will you let me milk your Moiley cow?'

'An' why wad you wish to milk wee Moiley, Grace, dear?' inquired Mrs Hanlon.

'Oh, just becase you're sae throng at the present time.'

'Thank you kindly, Grace, but I'm no too throng to do my ain work. I'll no trouble you to milk.'

The girl turned away with a discontented air; but the next evening, and the next, found her at the cow-house door with the same request.

At length Mrs Hanlon, not knowing well how to persist in her refusal, yielded, and permitted Grace to milk the Kerry cow.

She soon had reason to regret her want of firmness. Moiley gave no more milk to her owner.

When this melancholy state of things lasted for three days, the Hanlons applied to a certain Mark McCarrion, who lived near Binion.

'That cow has been milked by someone with an evil eye,' said he. 'Will she give you a wee drop, do you think? The full of a pint measure wad do.'

'Oh, ay, Mark, dear; I'll get that much milk frae her, any way.'

'Weel, Mrs Hanlon, lock the door, an' get nine new pins that was

BEWITCHED BUTTER

never used in clothes, an' put them into a saucepan wi' the pint o' milk. Set them on the fire, an' let them come to the boil.'

The nine pins soon began to simmer in Moiley's[1] milk.

Rapid steps were heard approaching the door, agitated knocks followed, and Grace Dogherty's high-toned voice was raised in eager entreaty.

'Let me in, Mrs Hanlon!' she cried. 'Tak off that cruel pot! Tak out them pins, for they're pricking holes in my heart, an' I'll never offer to touch milk of yours again.'

[There is hardly a village in Ireland where the milk is not thus believed to have been stolen times upon times. There are many counter-charms. Sometimes the coulter of a plough will be heated red-hot, and the witch will rush in, crying out that she is burning. A new horse-shoe or donskey-shoe, heated and put under the churn, with three straws, if possible, stolen at midnight from over the witches' door, is quite infallible. – Ed.]

---

1 In Connaught called a 'mweeal' cow – i.e., a cow without horns. Irish *maol*, literally, blunt. When the new hammerless breech-loaders came into use two or three years ago, Mr. Douglas Hyde heard a Connaught gentleman speak of them as the 'mweeal' guns, because they had no cocks.

A QUEEN'S COUNTY WITCH[1]

It was about eighty years ago, in the month of May, that a Roman Catholic clergyman, near Rathdowney, in the Queen's County, was awakened at midnight to attend a dying man in a distant part of the parish. The priest obeyed without a murmur, and having performed his duty to the expiring sinner, saw him depart this world before he left the cabin. As it was yet dark, the man who had called on the priest offered to accompany him home, but he refused, and set forward on his journey alone. The grey dawn began to appear over the hills. The good priest was highly enraptured with the beauty of the scene, and rode on, now gazing intently at every surrounding object, and again cutting with his whip at the bats and big beautiful night-flies which flitted ever and anon from hedge to hedge across his lonely way. Thus engaged, he journeyed on slowly, until the nearer approach of sunrise began to render objects completely discernible, when he dismounted from his horse, and slipping his arm out of the rein, and drawing forth his 'Breviary' from his pocket, he commenced reading his 'morning office' as he walked leisurely along.

He had not proceeded very far, when he observed his horse, a very spirited animal, endeavouring to stop on the road, and gazing intently into a field on one side of the way where there were three or four cows grazing. However, he did not pay any particular attention to this circumstance, but went on a little farther, when the horse suddenly plunged with great violence, and endeavoured to break away by force. The priest with great difficulty succeeded in restraining him, and, looking at him more closely, observed him shaking from head to foot, and sweating profusely. He now stood calmly, and refused to move

1 *Dublin University Review*, 1839.

A QUEEN'S COUNTY WITCH

from where he was, nor could threats or entreaty induce him to proceed. The father was greatly astonished, but recollecting to have often heard of horses labouring under affright being induced to go by blindfolding them, he took out his handkerchief and tied it across his eyes. He then mounted, and, striking him gently, he went forward without reluctance, but still sweating and trembling violently. They had not gone far, when they arrived opposite a narrow path or bridle-way, flanked at either side by a tall, thick hedge, which led from the high road to the field where the cows were grazing. The priest happened by chance to look into the lane, and saw a spectacle which made the blood curdle in his veins. It was the legs of a man from the hips downwards, without head or body, trotting up the avenue at a smart pace. The good father was very much alarmed, but, being a man of strong nerve, he resolved, come what might, to stand, and be further acquainted with this singular spectre. He accordingly stood, and so did the headless apparition, as if afraid to approach him. The priest, observing this, pulled back a little from the entrance of the avenue, and the phantom again resumed its progress. It soon arrived on the road, and the priest now had sufficient opportunity to view it minutely. It wore yellow buckskin breeches, tightly fastened at the knees with green ribbon; it had neither shoes nor stockings on, and its legs were covered with long, red hairs, and all full of wet, blood, and clay, apparently contracted in its progress through the thorny hedges. The priest, although very much alarmed, felt eager to examine the phantom, and for this purpose summoned all his philosophy to enable him to speak to it. The ghost was now a little ahead, pursuing its march at its usual brisk trot, and the priest urged on his horse speedily until he came up with it, and thus addressed it –

'Hilloa, friend! who art thou, or whither art thou going so early?'

The hideous spectre made no reply, but uttered a fierce and superhuman growl, or 'Umph.'

'A fine morning for ghosts to wander abroad,' again said the priest.

Another 'Umph' was the reply.

'Why don't you speak?'

'Umph.'

'You don't seem disposed to be very loquacious this morning.'

THE MAGICAL FOLK OF IRELAND

'Umph,' again.

The good man began to feel irritated at the obstinate silence of his unearthly visitor, and said, with some warmth –

'In the name of all that's sacred, I command you to answer me, Who art thou, or where art thou travelling?'

Another 'Umph,' more loud and more angry than before, was the only reply.

'Perhaps,' said the father, 'a taste of whipcord might render you a little more communicative'; and so saying, he struck the apparition a heavy blow with his whip on the breech.

The phantom uttered a wild and unearthly yell, and fell forward on the road, and what was the priest's astonishment when he perceived the whole place running over with milk. He was struck dumb with amazement; the prostrate phantom still continued to eject vast quantities of milk from every part; the priest's head swam, his eyes got dizzy; a stupor came all over him for some minutes, and on his recovering, the frightful spectre had vanished, and in its stead he found stretched on the road, and half drowned in milk, the form of Sarah Kennedy, an old woman of the neighbourhood, who had been long notorious in that district for her witchcraft and superstitious practices, and it was now discovered that she had, by infernal aid, assumed that monstrous shape, and was employed that morning in sucking the cows of the village. Had a volcano burst forth at his feet, he could not be more astonished; he gazed awhile in silent amazement – the old woman groaning, and writhing convulsively.

'Sarah,' said he, at length, 'I have long admonished you to repent of your evil ways, but you were deaf to my entreaties; and now, wretched woman, you are surprised in the midst of your crimes.'

'Oh, father, father,' shouted the unfortunate woman, 'can you do nothing to save me? I am lost; hell is open for me, and legions of devils surround me this moment, waiting to carry my soul to perdition.'

The priest had not power to reply; the old wretch's pains increased; her body swelled to an immense size; her eyes flashed as if on fire, her face was black as night, her entire form writhed in a thousand different contortions; her out-cries were appalling, her face sunk, her eyes

A QUEEN'S COUNTY WITCH

closed, and in a few minutes she expired in the most exquisite tortures.

The priest departed homewards, and called at the next cabin to give notice of the strange circumstances. The remains of Sarah Kennedy were removed to her cabin, situated at the edge of a small wood at a little distance. She had long been a resident in that neighbourhood, but still she was a stranger, and came there no one knew from whence. She had no relation in that country but one daughter, now advanced in years, who resided with her. She kept one cow, but sold more butter, it was said, than any farmer in the parish, and it was generally suspected that she acquired it by devilish agency, as she never made a secret of being intimately acquainted with sorcery and fairyism. She professed the Roman Catholic religion, but never complied with the practices enjoined by that church, and her remains were denied Christian sepulture, and were buried in a sand-pit near her own cabin.

On the evening of her burial, the villagers assembled and burned her cabin to the earth. Her daughter made her escape, and never after returned.

THE WITCH HARE

Mr and Mrs S. C. Hall

I was out thracking hares meeself, and I seen a fine puss of a thing hopping, hopping in the moonlight, and whacking her ears about, now up, now down, and winking her great eyes, and – 'Here goes,' says I, and the thing was so close to me that she turned round and looked at me, and then bounced back, as well as to say, do your worst! So I had the least grain in life of blessed powder left, and I put it in the gun – and bang at her! My jewel, the scritch she gave would frighten a rigment, and a mist, like, came betwixt me and her, and I seen her no more; but when the mist wint off I saw blood on the spot where she had been, and I followed its track, and at last it led me – whist, whisper – right up to Katey MacShane's door; and when I was at the thrashold, I heerd a murnin' within, a great murnin', and a groanin', and I opened the door, and there she was herself, sittin' quite content in the shape of a woman, and the black cat that was sittin' by her rose up its back and spit at me; but I went on never heedin', and asked the ould — how she was and what ailed her.

'Nothing,' sis she.

'What's that on the floor?' sis I.

'Oh,' she says, 'I was cuttin' a billet of wood,' she says, 'wid the reaping hook,' she says, 'an' I've wounded meself in the leg,' she says, 'and that's drops of my precious blood,' she says.

BEWITCHED BUTTER
(QUEEN'S COUNTY)[1]

About the commencement of the last century there lived in the vicinity of the once famous village of Aghavoe[2] a wealthy farmer, named Bryan Costigan. This man kept an extensive dairy and a great many milch cows, and every year made considerable sums by the sale of milk and butter. The luxuriance of the pasture lands in this neighbourhood has always been proverbial; and, consequently, Bryan's cows were the finest and most productive in the country, and his milk and butter the richest and sweetest, and brought the highest price at every market at which he offered these articles for sale.

Things continued to go on thus prosperously with Bryan Costigan, when, one season, all at once, he found his cattle declining in appearance, and his dairy almost entirely profitless. Bryan, at first, attributed this change to the weather, or some such cause, but soon found or fancied reasons to assign it to a far different source. The cows, without any visible disorder, daily declined, and were scarcely able to crawl about on their pasture: many of them, instead of milk, gave nothing but blood; and the scanty quantity of milk which some of them continued to supply was so bitter that even the pigs would not drink it; whilst the butter which it produced was of such a bad quality, and stunk so horribly,

---

1 *Dublin University Magazine*, 1839.

2 *Aghavoe* – 'the field of kine' – a beautiful and romantic village near Borris-in-Ossory, in the Queen's County. It was once a place of considerable importance, and for centuries the episcopal seat of the diocese of Ossory, but for ages back it has gone to decay, and is now remarkable for nothing but the magnificent ruins of a priory of the Dominicans, erected here at an early period by St Canice, the patron saint of Ossory.

THE MAGICAL FOLK OF IRELAND

that the very dogs would not eat it. Bryan applied for remedies to all the quacks and 'fairy-women' in the country – but in vain. Many of the impostors declared that the mysterious malady in his cattle went beyond *their* skill; whilst others, although they found no difficulty in tracing it to superhuman agency, declared that they had no control in the matter, as the charm under the influence of which his property was made away with, was too powerful to be dissolved by anything less than the special interposition of Divine Providence. The poor farmer became almost distracted; he saw ruin staring him in the face; yet what was he to do? Sell his cattle and purchase others! No; that was out of the question, as they looked so miserable and emaciated, that no one would even take them as a present, whilst it was also impossible to sell to a butcher, as the flesh of one which he killed for his own family was as black as a coal, and stunk like any putrid carrion.

The unfortunate man was thus completely bewildered. He knew not what to do; he became moody and stupid; his sleep forsook him by night, and all day he wandered about the fields, amongst his 'fairy-stricken' cattle like a maniac.

Affairs continued in this plight, when one very sultry evening in the latter days of July, Bryan Costigan's wife was sitting at her own door, spinning at her wheel, in a very gloomy and agitated state of mind. Happening to look down the narrow green lane which led from the high road to her cabin, she espied a little old woman barefoot, and enveloped in an old scarlet cloak, approaching slowly, with the aid of a crutch which she carried in one hand, and a cane or walking-stick in the other. The farmer's wife felt glad at seeing the odd-looking stranger; she smiled, and yet she knew not why, as she neared the house. A vague and indefinable feeling of pleasure crowded on her imagination; and, as the old woman gained the threshold, she bade her 'welcome' with a warmth which plainly told that her lips gave utterance but to the genuine feelings of her heart.

'God bless this good house and all belonging to it,' said the stranger as she entered.

'God save you kindly, and you are welcome, whoever you are,' replied Mrs Costigan.

BEWITCHED BUTTER

'Hem, I thought so,' said the old woman with a significant grin. 'I thought so, or I wouldn't trouble you.'

The farmer's wife ran, and placed a chair near the fire for the stranger; but she refused, and sat on the ground near where Mrs C. had been spinning. Mrs Costigan had now time to survey the old hag's person minutely. She appeared of great age; her countenance was extremely ugly and repulsive; her skin was rough and deeply embrowned as if from long exposure to the effects of some tropical climate; her forehead was low, narrow, and indented with a thousand wrinkles; her long grey hair fell in matted elf-locks from beneath a white linen skull-cap; her eyes were bleared, blood-shotten, and obliquely set in their sockets, and her voice was croaking, tremulous, and, at times, partially inarticulate. As she squatted on the floor, she looked round the house with an inquisitive gaze; she peered pryingly from corner to corner, with an earnestness of look, as if she had the faculty, like the Argonaut of old, to see through the very depths of the earth, whilst Mrs C. kept watching her motions with mingled feelings of curiosity, awe and pleasure.

'Mrs,' said the old woman, at length breaking silence, 'I am dry with the heat of the day; can you give me a drink?'

'Alas!' replied the farmer's wife, 'I have no drink to offer you except water, else you would have no occasion to ask me for it.'

'Are you not the owner of the cattle I see yonder?' said the old hag, with a tone of voice and manner of gesticulation which plainly indicated her foreknowledge of the fact.

Mrs Costigan replied in the affirmative, and briefly related to her every circumstance connected with the affair, whilst the old woman still remained silent, but shook her grey head repeatedly; and still continued gazing round the house with an air of importance and self-sufficiency.

When Mrs C. had ended, the old hag remained a while as if in a deep reverie: at length she said –

'Have you any of the milk in the house?'

'I have,' replied the other.

'Show me some of it.'

She filled a jug from a vessel and handed it to the old sybil, who smelled it, then tasted it, and spat out what she had taken on the floor.

THE MAGICAL FOLK OF IRELAND

'Where is your husband?' she asked.

'Out in the fields,' was the reply.

'I must see him.'

A messenger was despatched for Bryan, who shortly after made his appearance.

'Neighbour,' said the stranger, 'your wife informs me that your cattle are going against you this season.'

'She informs you right,' said Bryan.

'And why have you not sought a cure?'

'A cure!' re-echoed the man; 'why, woman, I have sought cures until I was heart-broken, and all in vain; they get worse every day.'

'What will you give me if I cure them for you?'

'Anything in our power,' replied Bryan and his wife, both speaking joyfully, and with a breath.

'All I will ask from you is a silver sixpence, and that you will do everything which I will bid you,' said she.

The farmer and his wife seemed astonished at the moderation of her demand. They offered her a large sum of money.

'No,' said she, 'I don't want your money; I am no cheat, and I would not even take sixpence, but that I can do nothing till I handle some of your silver.'

The sixpence was immediately given her, and the most implicit obedience promised to her injunctions by both Bryan and his wife, who already began to regard the old beldame as their tutelary angel.

The hag pulled off a black silk ribbon or fillet which encircled her head inside her cap, and gave it to Bryan, saying –

'Go, now, and the first cow you touch with this ribbon, turn her into the yard, but be sure don't touch the second, nor speak a word until you return; be also careful not to let the ribbon touch the ground, for, if you do, all is over.'

Bryan took the talismanic ribbon, and soon returned, driving a red cow before him.

The old hag went out, and, approaching the cow, commenced pulling hairs out of her tail, at the same time singing some verses in the Irish language in a low, wild and unconnected strain. The cow appeared

BEWITCHED BUTTER

restive and uneasy, but the old witch still continued her mysterious chant until she had the ninth hair extracted. She then ordered the cow to be drove back to her pasture, and again entered the house.

'Go, now,' said she to the woman, 'and bring me some milk from every cow in your possession.'

She went, and soon returned with a large pail filled with a frightful-looking mixture of milk, blood, and corrupt matter. The old woman got it into the churn, and made preparations for churning.

'Now,' she said, 'you both must churn, make fast the door and windows, and let there be no light but from the fire; do not open your lips until I desire you, and by observing my directions, I make no doubt but, ere the sun goes down, we will find out the infernal villain who is robbing you.'

Bryan secured the doors and windows, and commenced churning. The old sorceress sat down by a blazing fire which had been specially lighted for the occasion, and commenced singing the same wild song which she had sung at the pulling of the cow-hairs, and after a little time she cast one of the nine hairs into the fire, still singing her mysterious strain, and watching, with intense interest, the witching process.

A loud cry, as if from a female in distress, was now heard approaching the house; the old witch discontinued her incantations, and listened attentively. The crying voice approached the door.

'Open the door quickly,' shouted the charmer.

Bryan unbarred the door, and all three rushed out in the yard, when they heard the same cry down the *boreheen*, but could see nothing.

'It is all over,' shouted the old witch; 'something has gone amiss, and our charm for the present is ineffectual.'

They now turned back quite crest-fallen, when, as they were entering the door, the sybil cast her eyes downwards, and perceiving a piece of horse-shoe nailed on the threshold,[3] she vociferated –

---

3 It was once a common practice in Ireland to nail a piece of horse-shoe on the threshold of the door, as a preservative against the influence of the fairies, who, it is thought, dare not enter any house thus yarded. This custom, however, is much on the wane, but still it is prevalent in some of the more uncivilised districts of the country.

THE MAGICAL FOLK OF IRELAND

'Here I have it; no wonder our charm was abortive. The person that was crying abroad is the villain who has your cattle bewitched; I brought her to the house, but she was not able to come to the door on account of that horse-shoe. Remove it instantly, and we will try our luck again.'

Bryan removed the horse-shoe from the doorway, and by the hag's directions placed it on the floor under the churn, having previously reddened it in the fire.

They again resumed their manual operations. Bryan and his wife began to churn, and the witch again to sing her strange verses, and casting her cow-hairs into the fire until she had them all nearly exhausted. Her countenance now began to exhibit evident traces of vexation and disappointment. She got quite pale, her teeth gnashed, her hand trembled, and as she cast the ninth and last hair into the fire, her person exhibited more the appearance of a female demon than of a human being.

Once more the cry was heard, and an aged red-haired woman[4] was seen approaching the house quickly.

'Ho, ho!' roared the sorceress, 'I knew it would be so; my charm has succeeded; my expectations are realised, and here she comes, the villain who has destroyed you.'

'What are we to do now?' asked Bryan.

'Say nothing to her,' said the hag; 'give her whatever she demands, and leave the rest to me.'

The woman advanced screeching vehemently, and Bryan went out to meet her. She was a neighbour, and she said that one of her best cows was drowning in a pool of water – that there was no one at home but herself, and she implored Bryan to go rescue the cow from destruction.

Bryan accompanied her without hesitation; and having rescued the cow from her perilous situation, was back again in a quarter of an hour.

It was now sunset, and Mrs Costigan set about preparing supper.

---

4 Red-haired people are thought to possess magic power.

BEWITCHED BUTTER

During supper they reverted to the singular transactions of the day. The old witch uttered many a fiendish laugh at the success of her incantations, and inquired who was the woman whom they had so curiously discovered.

Bryan satisfied her in every particular. She was the wife of a neighbouring farmer; her name was Rachel Higgins; and she had been long suspected to be on familiar terms with the spirit of darkness. She had five or six cows; but it was observed by her sapient neighbours that she sold more butter every year than other farmers' wives who had twenty. Bryan had, from the commencement of the decline in his cattle, suspected her for being the aggressor, but as he had no proof, he held his peace.

'Well,' said the old beldame, with a grim smile, 'it is not enough that we have merely discovered the robber; all is in vain, if we do not take steps to punish her for the past, as well as to prevent her inroads for the future.'

'And how will that be done?' said Bryan.

'I will tell you; as soon as the hour of twelve o'clock arrives tonight, do you go to the pasture, and take a couple of swift-running dogs with you; conceal yourself in some place convenient to the cattle; watch them carefully; and if you see anything, whether man or beast, approach the cows, set on the dogs, and if possible make them draw the blood of the intruder; then all will be accomplished. If nothing approaches before sunrise, you may return, and we will try something else.'

Convenient there lived the cow-herd of a neighbouring squire. He was a hardy, courageous young man, and always kept a pair of very ferocious bull-dogs. To him Bryan applied for assistance, and he cheerfully agreed to accompany him, and, moreover, proposed to fetch a couple of his master's best greyhounds, as his own dogs, although extremely fierce and bloodthirsty, could not be relied on for swiftness. He promised Bryan to be with him before twelve o'clock, and they parted.

Bryan did not seek sleep that night; he sat up anxiously awaiting the midnight hour. It arrived at last, and his friend, the herdsman, true to his promise, came at the time appointed. After some further

THE MAGICAL FOLK OF IRELAND

admonitions from the *Collough*, they departed. Having arrived at the field, they consulted as to the best position they could chose for concealment. At last they pitched on a small brake of fern, situated at the extremity of the field, adjacent to the boundary ditch, which was thickly studded with large, old white-thorn bushes. Here they crouched themselves, and made the dogs, four in number, lie down beside them, eagerly expecting the appearance of their as yet unknown and mysterious visitor.

Here Bryan and his comrade continued a considerable time in nervous anxiety, still nothing approached, and it became manifest that morning was at hand; they were beginning to grow impatient, and were talking of returning home, when on a sudden they heard a rushing sound behind them, as if proceeding from something endeavouring to force a passage through the thick hedge in their rear. They looked in that direction, and judge of their astonishment, when they perceived a large hare in the act of springing from the ditch, and leaping on the ground quite near them. They were now convinced that this was the object which they had so impatiently expected, and they were resolved to watch her motions narrowly.

After arriving to the ground, she remained motionless for a few moments, looking around her sharply. She then began to skip and jump in a playful manner; now advancing at a smart pace towards the cows, and again retreating precipitately, but still drawing nearer and nearer at each sally. At length she advanced up to the next cow, and sucked her for a moment; then on to the next, and so respectively to every cow on the field – the cows all the time lowing loudly, and appearing extremely frightened and agitated. Bryan, from the moment the hare commenced sucking the first, was with difficulty restrained from attacking her; but his more sagacious companion suggested to him, that it was better to wait until she would have done, as she would then be much heavier, and more unable to effect her escape than at present. And so the issue proved; for being now done sucking them all, her belly appeared enormously distended, and she made her exit slowly and apparently with difficulty. She advanced towards the hedge where she had entered, and as she arrived just at the clump of ferns where her

BEWITCHED BUTTER

foes were couched, they started up with a fierce yell, and hallooed the dogs upon her path.

The hare started off at a brisk pace, squirting up the milk she had sucked from her mouth and nostrils, and the dogs making after her rapidly. Rachel Higgins's cabin appeared, through the grey of the morning twilight, at a little distance; and it was evident that puss seemed bent on gaining it, although she made a considerable circuit through the fields in the rear. Bryan and his comrade, however, had their thoughts, and made towards the cabin by the shortest route, and had just arrived as the hare came up, panting and almost exhausted, and the dogs at her very scut. She ran round the house, evidently confused and disappointed at the presence of the men, but at length made for the door. In the bottom of the door was a small, semi-circular aperture, resembling those cut in fowl-house doors for the ingress and egress of poultry. To gain this hole, puss now made a last and desperate effort, and had succeeded in forcing her head and shoulders through it, when the foremost of the dogs made a spring and seized her violently by the haunch. She uttered a loud and piercing scream, and struggled desperately to free herself from his gripe, and at last succeeded, but not until she left a piece of her rump in his teeth. The men now burst open the door; a bright turf fire blazed on the hearth, and the whole floor was streaming with blood. No hare, however, could be found, and the men were more than ever convinced that it was old Rachel, who had, by the assistance of some demon, assumed the form of the hare, and they now determined to have her if she were over the earth. They entered the bedroom, and heard some smothered groaning, as if proceeding from some one in extreme agony. They went to the corner of the room from whence the moans proceeded, and there, beneath a bundle of freshly cut rushes, found the form of Rachel Higgins, writhing in the most excruciating agony, and almost smothered in a pool of blood. The men were astounded; they addressed the wretched old woman, but she either could not, or would not answer them. Her wound still bled copiously; her tortures appeared to increase, and it was evident that she was dying. The aroused family thronged around her with cries and lamentations; she did not seem to heed them, she

THE MAGICAL FOLK OF IRELAND

got worse and worse, and her piercing yells fell awfully on the ears of the bystanders. At length she expired, and her corpse exhibited a most appalling spectacle, even before the spirit had well departed.

Bryan and his friend returned home. The old hag had been previously aware of the fate of Rachel Higgins, but it was not known by what means she acquired her supernatural knowledge. She was delighted at the issue of her mysterious operations. Bryan pressed her much to accept of some remuneration for her services, but she utterly rejected such proposals. She remained a few days at his house, and at length took her leave and departed, no one knew whither.

Old Rachel's remains were interred that night in the neighbouring churchyard. Her fate soon became generally known, and her family, ashamed to remain in their native village, disposed of their property, and quitted the country for ever. The story, however, is still fresh in the memory of the surrounding villagers; and often, it is said, amid the grey haze of a summer twilight, may the ghost of Rachel Higgins, in the form of a hare, be seen scudding over her favourite and well-remembered haunts.

THE WITCHES' EXCURSION[1]

Patrick Kennedy

Shemus Rua[2] (Red James) [was] awakened from his sleep one night by noises in his kitchen. Stealing to the door, he saw half-a-dozen old women sitting round the fire, jesting and laughing, his old housekeeper, Madge, quite frisky and gay, helping her sister crones to cheering glasses of punch. He began to admire the impudence and imprudence of Madge, displayed in the invitation and the riot, but recollected on the instant her officiousness in urging him to take a comfortable posset, which she had brought to his bedside just before he fell asleep. Had he drunk it, he would have been just now deaf to the witches' glee. He heard and saw them drink his health in such a mocking style as nearly to tempt him to charge them, besom in hand, but he restrained himself.

The jug being emptied, one of them cried out, 'Is it time to be gone?' and at the same moment, putting on a red cap, she added –

> 'By yarrow and rue,
> And my red cap too,
> Hie over to England.'

Making use of a twig which she held in her hand as a steed, she gracefully soared up the chimney, and was rapidly followed by the rest. But when it came to the housekeeper, Shemus interposed. 'By your leave, ma'am,' said he, snatching twig and cap. 'Ah, you desateful

---

1 *Fictions of the Irish Celts.*

2 Irish, *Séumus Ruadh*. The Celtic vocal organs are unable to pronounce the letter j, hence they make Shon or Shawn of John, or Shamus of James, etc.

ould crocodile! If I find you here on my return, there'll be wigs on the green –

> "By yarrow and rue,
> And my red cap too,
> Hie over to England."

The words were not out of his mouth when he was soaring above the ridge pole, and swiftly ploughing the air. He was careful to speak no word (being somewhat conversant with witch-lore), as the result would be a tumble, and the immediate return of the expedition.

In a very short time they had crossed the Wicklow hills, the Irish Sea, and the Welsh mountains, and were charging, at whirlwind speed, the hall door of a castle. Shemus, only for the company in which he found himself, would have cried out for pardon, expecting to be *mummy* against the hard oak door in a moment; but, all bewildered, he found himself passing through the keyhole, along a passage, down a flight of steps, and through a cellar-door key-hole before he could form any clear idea of his situation.

Waking to the full consciousness of his position, he found himself sitting on a stillion, plenty of lights glimmering round, and he and his companions, with full tumblers of frothing wine in hand, hob-nobbing and drinking healths as jovially and recklessly as if the liquor was honestly come by, and they were sitting in *Shemus's* own kitchen. The red birredh[3] had assimilated *Shemus's* nature for the time being to that of his unholy companions. The heady liquors soon got into their brains, and a period of unconsciousness succeeded the ecstasy, the head-ache, the turning round of the barrels, and the 'scattered sight ' of poor Shemus. He woke up under the impression of being roughly seized, and shaken, and dragged upstairs, and subjected to a disagreeable examination by the lord of the castle, in his state parlour. There was much derision among the whole company, gentle and simple, on hearing Shemus's explanation, and, as the thing occurred in the dark

---

3 Ir., *Birreud* – i.e., a cap.

THE WITCHES' EXCURSION

ages, the unlucky Leinster man was sentenced to be hung as soon as the gallows could be prepared for the occasion.

The poor Hibernian was in the cart proceeding on his last journey, with a label on his back, and another on his breast, announcing him as the remorseless villain who for the last month had been draining the casks in my lord's vault every night. He was surprised to hear himself addressed by his name, and in his native tongue, by an old woman in the crowd. 'Ach, Shemus, alanna! is it going to die you are in a strange place without your *cappeen d'yarrag*?'[4] These words infused hope and courage into the poor victim's heart. He turned to the lord and humbly asked leave to die in his red cap, which he supposed had dropped from his head in the vault. A servant was sent for the head-piece, and Shemus felt lively hope warming his heart while placing it on his head. On the platform he was graciously allowed to address the spectators, which he proceeded to do in the usual formula composed for the benefit of flying stationers – 'Good people all, a warning take by me'; but when he had finished the line, 'My parents reared me tenderly,' he unexpectedly added – 'By yarrow and rue,' etc., and the disappointed spectators saw him shoot up obliquely through the air in the style of a sky-rocket that had missed its aim. It is said that the lord took the circumstance much to heart, and never afterwards hung a man for twenty-four hours after his offence.

4 Irish, *caipín dearg* – i.e., red cap.

THE CONFESSIONS OF TOM BOURKE

T. Crofton Croker

Tom Bourke lives in a low, long farm-house, resembling in outward appearance a large barn, placed at the bottom of the hill, just where the new road strikes off from the old one, leading from the town of Kilworth to that of Lismore. He is of a class of persons who are a sort of black swans in Ireland: he is a wealthy farmer. Tom's father had, in the good old times, when a hundred pounds were no inconsiderable treasure, either to lend or spend, accommodated his landlord with that sum, at interest; and obtained as a return for his civility a long lease, about half-a-dozen times more valuable than the loan which procured it. The old man died worth several hundred pounds, the greater part of which, with his farm, he bequeathed to his son Tom. But besides all this, Tom received from his father, upon his death-bed, another gift, far more valuable than worldly riches, greatly as he prized and is still known to prize them. He was invested with the privilege, enjoyed by few of the sons of men, of communicating with those mysterious beings called 'the good people'.

Tom Bourke is a little, stout, healthy, active man, about fifty-five years of age. His hair is perfectly white, short and bushy behind, but rising in front erect and thick above his forehead, like a new clothes-brush. His eyes are of that kind which I have often observed with persons of a quick, but limited intellect – they are small, grey, and lively. The large and projecting eyebrows under, or rather within, which they twinkle, give them an expression of shrewdness and intelligence, if not of cunning. And this is very much the character of the man. If you want to make a bargain with Tom Bourke you must act as if you were a general besieging a town, and make your advances a

THE CONFESSIONS OF TOM BOURKE

long time before you can hope to obtain possession; if you march up boldly, and tell him at once your object, you are for the most part sure to have the gates closed in your teeth. Tom does not wish to part with what you wish to obtain; or another person has been speaking to him for the whole of the last week. Or, it may be, your proposal seems to meet the most favourable reception. 'Very well, sir'; 'That's true, sir'; 'I'm very thankful to your honour', and other expressions of kindness and confidence greet you in reply to every sentence; and you part from him wondering how he can have obtained the character which he universally bears, of being a man whom no one can make anything of in a bargain. But when you next meet him the flattering illusion is dissolved: you find you are a great deal further from your object than you were when you thought you had almost succeeded; his eye and his tongue express a total forgetfulness of what the mind within never lost sight of for an instant; and you have to begin operations afresh, with the disadvantage of having put your adversary completely upon his guard.

Yet, although Tom Bourke is, whether from supernatural revealings, or (as many will think more probable) from the tell-truth experience, so distrustful of mankind, and so close in his dealings with them, he is no misanthrope. No man loves better the pleasures of the genial board. The love of money, indeed, which is with him (and who will blame him?) a very ruling propensity, and the gratification which it has received from habits of industry, sustained throughout a pretty long and successful life, have taught him the value of sobriety, during those seasons, at least, when a man's business requires him to keep possession of his senses. He has, therefore, a general rule, never to get drunk but on Sundays. But in order that it should be a general one to all intents and purposes, he takes a method which, according to better logicians than he is, always proves the rule. He has many exceptions; among these, of course, are the evenings of all the fair and market-days that happen in his neighbourhood; so also all the days in which funerals, marriages and christenings take place among his friends within many miles of him. As to this last class of exceptions, it may appear at first very singular, that he is much more punctual in

THE MAGICAL FOLK OF IRELAND

his attendance at the funerals than at the baptisms or weddings of his friends. This may be construed as an instance of disinterested affection for departed worth, very uncommon in this selfish world. But I am afraid that the motives which lead Tom Bourke to pay more court to the dead than the living are precisely those which lead to the opposite conduct in the generality of mankind – a hope of future benefit and a fear of future evil. For the good people, who are a race as powerful as they are capricious, have their favourites among those who inhabit this world; often show their affection by easing the objects of it from the load of this burdensome life; and frequently reward or punish the living according to the degree of reverence paid to the obsequies and the memory of the elected dead.

Some may attribute to the same cause the apparently humane and charitable actions which Tom, and indeed the other members of his family, are known frequently to perform. A beggar has seldom left their farm-yard with an empty wallet, or without obtaining a night's lodging, if required, with a sufficiency of potatoes and milk to satisfy even an Irish beggar's appetite; in appeasing which, account must usually be taken of the auxiliary jaws of a hungry dog, and of two or three still more hungry children, who line themselves well within, to atone for their nakedness without. If one of the neighbouring poor be seized with a fever, Tom will often supply the sick wretch with some untenanted hut upon one of his two large farms (for he has added one to his patrimony), or will send his labourers to construct a shed at a hedge-side, and supply straw for a bed while the disorder continues. His wife, remarkable for the largeness of her dairy, and the goodness of everything it contains, will furnish milk for whey; and their good offices are frequently extended to the family of the patient, who are, perhaps, reduced to the extremity of wretchedness, by even the temporary suspension of a father's or a husband's labour.

If much of this arises from the hopes and fears to which I above alluded, I believe much of it flows from a mingled sense of compassion and of duty, which is sometimes seen to break from an Irish peasant's heart, even where it happens to be enveloped in a habitual covering of avarice and fraud; and which I once heard speak in terms not to be

THE CONFESSIONS OF TOM BOURKE

misunderstood: 'When we get a deal, 'tis only fair we should give back a little of it.'

It is not easy to prevail on Tom to speak of those good people, with whom he is said to hold frequent and intimate communications. To the faithful, who believe in their power, and their occasional delegation of it to him, he seldom refuses, if properly asked, to exercise his high prerogative when any unfortunate being is *struck* in his neighbourhood. Still he will not be won unsued: he is at first difficult of persuasion, and must be overcome by a little gentle violence. On these occasions he is unusually solemn and mysterious, and if one word of reward be mentioned he at once abandons the unhappy patient, such a proposition being a direct insult to his supernatural superiors. It is true that, as the labourer is worthy of his hire, most persons gifted as he is do not scruple to receive a token of gratitude from the patients or their friends *after* their recovery. It is recorded that a very handsome gratuity was once given to a female practitioner in this occult science, who deserves to be mentioned, not only because she was a neighbour and a rival of Tom's, but from the singularity of a mother deriving her name fiom her son. Her son's name was Owen, and she was always called *Owen sa vauher* (Owen's mother). This person was, on the occasion to which I have alluded, *persuaded* to give her assistance to a young girl who had lost the use of her right leg; *Owen sa vauher* found the cure a difficult one. A journey of about eighteen miles was essential for the purpose, probably to visit one of the good people who resided at that distance; and this journey could only be performed by *Owen sa vauher* travelling upon the back of a white hen. The visit, however, was accomplished; and at a particular hour, according to the prediction of this extraordinary woman, when the hen and her rider were to reach their journey's end, the patient was seized with an irresistible desire to dance, which she gratified with the most perfect freedom of the diseased leg, much to the joy of her anxious family. The gratuity in this case was, as it surely ought to have been, unusually large, from the difficulty of procuring a hen willing to go so long a journey with such a rider.

To do Tom Bourke justice, he is on these occasions, as I have heard from many competent authorities, perfectly disinterested. Not many

THE MAGICAL FOLK OF IRELAND

months since he recovered a young woman (the sister of a tradesman living near him), who had been struck speechless after returning from a funeral, and had continued so for several days. He steadfastly refused receiving any compensation, saying that even if he had not as much as would buy him his supper, he could take nothing in this case, because the girl had offended at the funeral of one of the good people belonging to his own family, and though he would do her a kindness, he could take none from her.

About the time this last remarkable affair took place, my friend Mr Martin, who is a neighbour of Tom's, had some business to transact with him, which it was exceedingly difficult to bring to a conclusion. At last Mr Martin, having tried all quiet means, had recourse to a legal process, which brought Tom to reason, and the matter was arranged to their mutual satisfaction, and with perfect good humour between the parties. The accommodation took place after dinner at Mr Martin's house, and he invited Tom to walk into the parlour and take a glass of punch, made of some excellent *poteen*, which was on the table: he had long wished to draw out his highly endowed neighbour on the subject of his supernatural powers, and as Mrs Martin, who was in the room, was rather a favourite of Tom's, this seemed a good opportunity.

'Well, Tom,' said Mr Martin, 'that was a curious business of Molly Dwyer's, who recovered her speech so suddenly the other day.'

'You may say that, sir,' replied Tom Bourke; 'but I had to travel far for it: no matter for that now. Your health, ma'am,' said he, turning to Mrs Martin.

'Thank you, Tom. But I am told you had some trouble once in that way in your own family,' said Mrs Martin.

'So I had, ma'am; trouble enough: but you were only a child at that time.'

'Come, Tom,' said the hospitable Mr Martin, interrupting him, 'take another tumbler'; and he then added, 'I wish you would tell us something of the manner in which so many of your children died. I am told they dropped off, one after another, by the same disorder, and that your eldest son was cured in a most extraordinary way, when the physicians had given him over.'

THE CONFESSIONS OF TOM BOURKE

"'Tis true for you, sir,' returned Tom; 'your father, the doctor (God be good to him, I won't belie him in his grave), told me, when my fourth boy was a week sick, that himself and Dr Barry did all that man could do for him; but they could not keep him from going after the rest. No more they could, if the people that took away the rest wished to take him too. But they left him; and sorry to the heart I am I did not know before why they were taking my boys from me; if I did, I would not be left trusting to two of 'em now.'

'And how did you find it out, Tom?' inquired Mr Martin.

'Why, then, I'll tell you, sir,' said Bourke. 'When your father said what I told you, I did not know very well what to do. I walked down the little *bohereen*[1] you know, sir, that goes to the river-side near Dick Heafy's ground; for 'twas a lonesome place, and I wanted to think of myself. I was heavy, sir, and my heart got weak in me, when I thought I was to lose my little boy; and I did not well know how to face his mother with the news, for she doted down upon him. Besides, she never got the better of all she cried at his brother's *berrin*[2] the week before. As I was going down the bohereen I met an old *bocough*, that used to come about the place once or twice a-year, and used always to sleep in our barn while he staid in the neighbourhood. So he asked me how I was. 'Bad enough, Shamous,'[3] says I. 'I'm sorry for your trouble,' says he; 'but you're a foolish man, Mr Bourke. Your son would be well enough if you would only do what you ought with him.' 'What more can I do with him, Shamous?' says I; 'the doctors give him over.' 'The doctors know no more what ails him than they do what ails a cow when she stops her milk,' says Shamous; 'but go to such a one,' telling me his name, 'and try what he'll say to you.''

'And who was that, Tom?' asked Mr Martin.

'I could not tell you that, sir,' said Bourke, with a mysterious look; 'howsomever, you often saw him, and he does not live far from this. But

---

1 *Bohereen*, or *bogheen*, i.e., a green lane.

2 *Berrin*, burying.

3 Shamous, James.

THE MAGICAL FOLK OF IRELAND

I had a trial of him before; and if I went to him at first, maybe I'd have now some of them that's gone, and so Shamous often told me. Well, sir, I went to this man, and he came with me to the house. By course, I did everything as he bid me. According to his order, I took the little boy out of the dwelling-house immediately, sick as he was, and made a bed for him and myself in the cow-house. Well, sir, I lay down by his side in the bed, between two of the cows, and he fell asleep. He got into a perspiration, saving your presence, as if he was drawn through the river, and breathed hard, with a great *impression* on his chest, and was very bad – very bad entirely through the night. I thought about twelve o'clock he was going at last, and I was just getting up to go call the man I told you of; but there was no occasion. My friends were getting the better of them that wanted to take him away from me. There was nobody in the cow-house but the child and myself. There was only one halfpenny candle lighting it, and that was stuck in the wall at the far end of the house. I had just enough of light where we were lying to see a person walking or standing near us: and there was no more noise than if it was a churchyard, except the cows chewing the fodder in the stalls.

Just as I was thinking of getting up, as I told you – I won't belie my father, sir, he was a good father to me – I saw him standing at the bedside, holding out his right hand to me, and leaning his other on the stick he used to carry when he was alive, and looking pleasant and smiling at me, all as if he was telling me not to be afeard, for I would not lose the child. 'Is that you, father?' says I. He said nothing. 'If that's you,' says I again, 'for the love of them that gone, let me catch your hand.' And so he did, sir; and his hand was as soft as a child's. He stayed about as long as you'd be going from this to the gate below at the end of the avenue, and then went away. In less than a week the child was as well as if nothing ever ailed him; and there isn't tonight a healthier boy of nineteen, from this blessed house to the town of Ballyporeen, across the Kilworth mountains.'

'But I think, Tom,' said Mr Martin, 'it appears as if you are more indebted to your father than to the man recommended to you by Shamous; or do you suppose it was he who made favour with your enemies among the good people, and that then your father –'

THE CONFESSIONS OF TOM BOURKE

'I beg your pardon, sir,' said Bourke, interrupting him; 'but don't call them my enemies. 'Twould not be wishing to me for a good deal to sit by when they are called so. No offence to you, sir. Here's wishing you a good health and long life.'

'I assure you,' returned Mr Martin, 'I meant no offence, Tom; but was it not as I say?'

'I can't tell you that, sir,' said Bourke; 'I'm bound down, sir. Howsoever, you may be sure the man I spoke of and my father, and those they know, settled it between them.'

There was a pause, of which Mrs Martin took advantage to inquire of Tom whether something remarkable had not happened about a goat and a pair of pigeons, at the time of his son's illness – circumstances often mysteriously hinted at by Tom.

'See that, now,' said he, turning to Mr Martin, 'how well she remembers it! True for you, ma'am. The goat I gave the mistress, your mother, when the doctors ordered her goats' whey?'

Mrs Martin nodded assent, and Tom Bourke continued, 'Why, then, I'll tell you how that was. The goat was as well as e'er goat ever was, for a month after she was sent to Killaan, to your father's. The morning after the night I just told you of, before the child woke, his mother was standing at the gap leading out of the barn-yard into the road, and she saw two pigeons flying from the town of Kilworth off the church down towards her. Well, they never stopped, you see, till they came to the house on the hill at the other side of the river, facing our farm. They pitched upon the chimney of that house, and after looking about them for a minute or two, they flew straight across the river, and stopped on the ridge of the cow-house where the child and I were lying. Do you think they came there for nothing, sir?'

'Certainly not, Tom,' returned Mr Martin.

'Well, the woman came in to me, frightened, and told me. She began to cry. "Whisht, you fool?" says I; "'tis all for the better." 'Twas true for me. What do you think, ma'am; the goat that I gave your mother, that was seen feeding at sunrise that morning by Jack Cronin, as merry as a bee, dropped down dead without anybody knowing why, before Jack's face; and at that very moment he saw two pigeons fly from the

THE MAGICAL FOLK OF IRELAND

top of the house out of the town, towards the Lismore road. 'Twas at the same time my woman saw them, as I just told you.'

''Twas very strange, indeed, Tom,' said Mr Martin; 'I wish you could give us some explanation of it.'

'I wish I could, sir,' was Tom Bourke's answer; 'but I'm bound down. I can't tell but what I'm allowed to tell, any more than a sentry is let walk more than his rounds.'

'I think you said something of having had some former knowledge of the man that assisted in the cure of your son,' said Mr Martin.

'So I had, sir,' returned Bourke. 'I had a trial of that man. But that's neither here nor there. I can't tell you anything about that, sir. But would you like to know how he got his skill?'

'Oh! very much, indeed,' said Mr Martin.

'But you can tell us his Christian name, that we may know him better through the story,' added Mrs Martin.

Tom Bourke paused for a minute to consider this proposition.

'Well, I believe that I may tell you that, anyhow; his name is Patrick. He was always a smart, 'cute[4] boy, and would be a great clerk if he stuck to it. The first time I knew him, sir, was at my mother's wake. I was in great trouble, for I did not know where to bury her. Her people and my father's people – I mean their friends, sir, among the *good people* – had the greatest battle that was known for many a year, at Dunmanwaycross, to see to whose church-yard she'd be taken. They fought for three nights, one after another, without being able to settle it. The neighbours wondered how long I was before I buried my mother; but I had my reasons, though I could not tell them at that time. Well, sir, to make my story short, Patrick came on the fourth morning and told me he settled the business, and that day we buried her in Kilcrumper churchyard, with my father's people.'

'He was a valuable friend, Tom,' said Mrs Martin, with difficulty suppressing a smile. 'But you were about to tell how he became so skilful.'

4 'Cute, acute.

THE CONFESSIONS OF TOM BOURKE

'So I will and welcome,' replied Bourke. 'Your health, ma'am. I'm drinking too much of this punch, sir; but to tell the truth, I never tasted the like of it; it goes down one's throat like sweet oil. But what was I going to say? Yes – well – Patrick, many a long year ago, was coming home from a *berrin* late in the evening, and walking by the side of a river, opposite the big inch,[5] near Ballyhefaan ford. He had taken a drop, to be sure; but he was only a little merry, as you may say, and knew very well what he was doing. The moon was shining, for it was in the month of August, and the river was as smooth and as bright as a looking-glass. He heard nothing for a long time but the fall of the water at the mill weir about a mile down the river, and now and then the crying of the lambs on the other side of the river. All at once there was a noise of a great number of people laughing as if they'd break their hearts, and of a piper playing among them. It came from the inch at the other side of the ford, and he saw, through the mist that hung over the river, a whole crowd of people dancing on the inch. Patrick was as fond of a dance, as he was of a glass, and that's saying enough for him; so he whipped off his shoes and stockings, and away with him across the ford. After putting on his shoes and stockings at the other side of the river he walked over to the crowd, and mixed with them for some time without being minded. He thought, sir, that he'd show them better dancing than any of themselves, for he was proud of his feet, sir, and a good right he had, for there was not a boy in the same parish could foot a double or treble with him. But pwah! his dancing was no more to theirs than mine would be to the mistress' there. They did not seem as if they had a bone in their bodies, and they kept it up as if nothing could tire them. Patrick was 'shamed within himself, for he thought he had not his fellow in all the country round; and was going away, when a little old man, that was looking at the company bitterly, as if he did not like what was going on, came up to him. 'Patrick,' says he. Patrick started, for he did not think anybody there knew him. 'Patrick,' says he, 'you're discouraged, and no wonder for you. But you have a friend

5 Inch, low meadow ground near a river.

167

THE MAGICAL FOLK OF IRELAND

near you. I'm your friend, and your father's friend, and I think worse[6] of your little finger than I do of all that are here, though they think no one is as good as themselves. Go into the ring and call for a lilt. Don't be afeard. I tell you the best of them did not do it as well as you shall, if you will do as I bid you.' Patrick felt something within him as if he ought not to gainsay the old man. He went into the ring, and called the piper to play up the best double he had. And sure enough, all that the others were able for was nothing to him! He bounded like an eel, now here and now there, as light as a feather, although the people could hear the music answered by his steps, that beat time to every turn of it, like the left foot of the piper. He first danced a hornpipe on the ground. Then they got a table, and he danced a treble on it that drew down shouts from the whole company. At last he called for a trencher; and when they saw him, all as if he was spinning on it like a top, they did not know what to make of him. Some praised him for the best dancer that ever entered a ring; others hated him because he was better than themselves; although they had good right to think themselves better than him or any other man that ever went the long journey.'

'And what was the cause of his great success?' inquired Mr Martin.

'He could not help it, sir,' replied Tom Bourke. 'They that could make him do more than that made him do it. Howsomever, when he had done, they wanted him to dance again, but he was tired, and they could not persuade him. At last he got angry, and swore a big oath, saving your presence, that he would not dance a step more; and the word was hardly out of his mouth when he found himself all alone, with nothing but a white cow grazing by his side.'

'Did he ever discover why he was gifted with these extraordinary powers in the dance, Tom?' said Mr Martin.

'I'll tell you that too, sir,' answered Bourke, 'when I come to it. When he went home, sir, he was taken with a shivering, and went to bed; and the next day they found he had got the fever, or something like it, for he raved like as if he was mad. But they couldn't make out

6 Worse, more.

168

THE CONFESSIONS OF TOM BOURKE

what it was he was saying, though he talked constant. The doctors gave him over. But it's little they knew what ailed him. When he was, as you may say, about ten days sick, and everybody thought he was going, one of the neighbours came in to him with a man, a friend of his, from Ballinlacken, that was keeping with him some time before. I can't tell you his name either, only it was Darby. The minute Darby saw Patrick he took a little bottle, with the juice of herbs in it, out of his pocket, and gave Patrick a drink of it. He did the same every day for three weeks, and then Patrick was able to walk about, as stout and as hearty as ever he was in his life. But he was a long time before he came to himself; and he used to walk the whole day sometimes by the ditch-side, talking to himself, like as if there was someone along with him. And so there was, surely, or he wouldn't be the man he is today.'

'I suppose it was from some such companion he learned his skill,' said Mr Martin.

'You have it all now, sir,' replied Bourke. 'Darby told him his friends were satisfied with what he did the night of the dance; and though they couldn't hinder the fever, they'd bring him over it, and teach him more than many knew beside him. And so they did. For you see, all the people he met on the inch that night were friends of a different faction; only the old man that spoke to him, he was a friend of Patrick's family, and it went again his heart, you see, that the others were so light and active, and he was bitter in himself to hear 'em boasting how they'd dance with any set in the whole country round. So he gave Patrick the gift that night, and afterwards gave him the skill that makes him the wonder of all that know him. And to be sure it was only learning he was at that time when he was wandering in his mind after the fever.'

'I have heard many strange stories about that inch near Ballyhefaan ford,' said Mr Martin. ''Tis a great place for the good people, isn't it, Tom?'

'You may say that, sir,' returned Bourke. 'I could tell you a great deal about it. Many a time I sat for as good as two hours by moonlight, at th' other side of the river, looking at 'em playing goal as if they'd break their hearts over it; with their coats and waistcoats off, and white handkerchiefs on the heads of one party, and red ones on th' other, just

THE MAGICAL FOLK OF IRELAND

as you'd see on a Sunday in Mr Simming's big field. I saw 'em one night play till the moon set, without one party being able to take the ball from th' other. I'm sure they were going to fight, only 'twas near morning. I'm told your grandfather, ma'am, used to see 'em there too,' said Bourke, turning to Mrs Martin.

'So I have been told, Tom,' replied Mrs Martin. 'But don't they say that the churchyard of Kilcrumper is just as favourite a place with the good people as Ballyhefaan inch?'

'Why, then, maybe you never heard, ma'am, what happened to Davy Roche in that same churchyard,' said Bourke; and turning to Mr Martin, added, ''Twas a long time before he went into your service, sir. He was walking home, of an evening, from the fair of Kilcumber, a little merry, to be sure, after the day, and he came up with a berrin. So he walked along with it, and thought it very queer that he did not know a mother's soul in the crowd but one man, and he was sure that man was dead many years afore. Howsomever, he went on with the berrin till they came to Kilcrumper churchyard; and, faith, he went in and stayed with the rest, to see the corpse buried. As soon as the grave was covered, what should they do but gather about a piper that come along with 'em, and fall to dancing as if it was a wedding. Davy longed to be among 'em (for he hadn't a bad foot of his own, that time, whatever he may now); but he was loth to begin, because they all seemed strange to him, only the man I told you that he thought was dead. Well, at last this man saw what Davy wanted, and came up to him. 'Davy,' says he, 'take out a partner, and show what you can do, but take care and don't offer to kiss her.' 'That I won't,' says Davy, 'although her lips were made of honey.' And with that he made his bow to the *purtiest* girl in the ring, and he and she began to dance. 'Twas a jig they danced, and they did it to th' admiration, do you see, of all that were there. 'Twas all very well till the jig was over; but just as they had done, Davy, for he had a drop in, and was warm with the dancing, forgot himself, and kissed his partner, according to custom. The smack was no sooner off of his lips, you see, than he was left alone in the churchyard, without a creature near him, and all he could see was the tall tombstones. Davy said they seemed as if they were dancing too, but I suppose that was only the

THE CONFESSIONS OF TOM BOURKE

wonder that happened him, and he being a little in drink. Howsomever, he found it was a great many hours later than he thought it; 'twas near morning when he came home; but they couldn't get a word out of him till the next day, when he woke out of a dead sleep about twelve o'clock.'

When Tom had finished the account of Davy Roche and the berrin, it became quite evident that spirits, of some sort, were working too strong within him to admit of his telling many more tales of the good people. Tom seemed conscious of this. He muttered for a few minutes broken sentences concerning churchyards, river-sides, leprechauns, and *dina magh*[7] which were quite unintelligible, perhaps, to himself, certainly to Mr Martin and his lady. At length he made a slight motion of the head upwards, as if he would say, 'I can talk no more'; stretched his arm on the table, upon which he placed the empty tumbler slowly, and with the most knowing and cautious air; and rising from his chair, walked, or rather rolled, to the parlour door. Here he turned round to face his host and hostess; but after various ineffectual attempts to bid them good-night, the words, as they rose, being always choked by a violent hiccup, while the door, which he held by the handle, swung to and fro, carrying his unyielding body along with it, he was obliged to depart in silence. The cow-boy, sent by Tom's wife, who knew well what sort of allurement detained him when he remained out after a certain hour, was in attendance to conduct his master home. I have no doubt that he returned without meeting any material injury, as I know that within the last month he was, to use his own words, 'as stout and hearty a man as any of his age in the county Cork.'

7 *Daoine maithe* – i.e. the good people.

THE PUDDING BEWITCHED

William Carleton

'Moll Roe Rafferty was the son – daughter I mane – of ould Jack Rafferty, who was remarkable for a habit he had of always wearing his head undher his hat; but indeed the same family was a quare one, as everybody knew that was acquainted wid them. It was said of them – but whether it was thrue or not I won't undhertake to say, for 'fraid I'd tell a lie – that whenever they didn't wear shoes or boots they always went barefooted; but I heard afthewards that this was disputed, so rather than say anything to injure their character, I'll let that pass. Now, ould Jack Rafferty had two sons, Paddy and Molly – hut! what are you all laughing at? – I mane a son and daughter, and it was generally believed among the neighbours that they were brother and. sisther, which you know might be thrue or it might not: but that's a thing that, wid the help o' goodness, we have nothing to say to. Troth there was many ugly things put out on them that I don't wish to repate, such as that neither Jack nor his son Paddy ever walked a perch widout puttin' one foot afore the other like a salmon; an' I know it was whispered about, that whinever Moll Roe slep', she had an out-of-the-way custom of keepin' her eyes shut. If she did, however, for that matther the loss was her own; for sure we all know that when one comes to shut their eyes they can't see as far before them as another.

'Moll Roe was a fine young bouncin' girl, large and lavish, wid a purty head o' hair on her like scarlet, that bein' one of the raisons why she was called *Roe*, or red; her arms an' cheeks were much the colour of the hair, an' her saddle nose was the purtiest thing of its kind that ever was on a face. Her fists – for, thank goodness, she was well sarved wid them too – had a strong similarity to two thumpin' turnips, reddened by the sun; an' to keep all right and tight, she had a temper as

THE PUDDING BEWITCHED

fiery as her head – for, indeed, it was well known that all the Rafferties were *warm*-hearted. Howandiver, it appears that God gives nothing in vain, and of coorse the same fists, big and red as they were, if all that is said about them is thrue, were not so much given to her for ornament as use. At laist, takin' them in connection wid her lively temper, we have it upon good authority, that there was no danger of their getting blue-moulded for want of practice. She had a twist, too, in one of her eyes that was very becomin' in its way, and made her poor husband, when she got him, take it into his head that she could see round a corner. She found him out in many quare things, widout doubt; but whether it was owin' to that or not, I wouldn't undertake to say *for fraid I'd tell a lie*.

'Well, begad, anyhow it was Moll Roe that was the *dilsy*.[1] It happened that there was a nate vagabone in the neighbourhood, just as much overburdened wid beauty as herself, and he was named Gusty Gillespie. Gusty, the Lord guard us, was what they call a black-mouth Prosbytarian, and wouldn't keep Christmas-day, the blagard, except what they call 'ould style'. Gusty was rather good-lookin' when seen in the dark, as well as Moll herself; and, indeed, it was purty well known that – accordin' as the talk went – it was in nightly meetings that they had an opportunity of becomin' detached to one another. The quensequence was, that in due time both families began to talk very seriously as to what was to be done. Moll's brother, Pawdien O'Rafferty, gave Gusty the best of two choices. What they were it's not worth spakin' about; but at any rate *one* of them was a poser, an' as Gusty knew his man, he soon came to his senses. Accordianly everything was deranged for their marriage, and it was appointed that they should be spliced by the Rev. Samuel M'Shuttle, the Prosbytarian parson, on the following Sunday.

'Now this was the first marriage that had happened for a long time in the neighbourhood betune a black-mouth an' a Catholic, an' of coorse there was strong objections on both sides aginst it; an' begad, only for one thing, it would never 'a tuck place at all. At any rate, faix, there

---

1 Perhaps from Irish *dilse* – i.e., love.

THE MAGICAL FOLK OF IRELAND

was one of the bride's uncles, ould Harry Connolly, a fairy-man, who could cure all complaints wid a secret he had, and as he didn't wish to see his niece married upon sich a fellow, he fought bittherly against the match. All Moll's friends, however, stood up for the marriage barrin' him, an' of coorse the Sunday was appointed, as I said, that they were to be dove-tailed together.

'Well, the day arrived, and Moll, as became her, went to mass, and Gusty to meeting, afther which they were to join one another in Jack Rafferty's, where the priest, Father M'Sorley, was to slip up afther mass to take his dinner wid them, and to keep Misther M'Shuttle, who was to marry them, company. Nobody remained at home but ould Jack Rafferty an' his wife, who stopped to dress the dinner, for, to tell the truth, it was to be a great let-out entirely. Maybe, if all was known, too, that Father M'Sorley was to give them a cast of his office over an' above the ministher, in regard that Moll's friends were not altogether satisfied at the kind of marriage which M'Shuttle could give them. The sorrow may care about that – splice here – splice there – all I can say is, that when Mrs Rafferty was goin' to tie up a big bag pudden, in walks Harry Connolly, the fairy-man, in a rage, and shouts out, – "Blood and blunderbushes, what are yez here for?"

'"Arrah why, Harry? Why, avick?"

'"Why, the sun's in the suds and the moon in the high Horicks; there's a clipstick comin' an, an' there you're both as unconsarned as if it was about to rain mether. Go out and cross yourselves three times in the name o' the four Mandromarvins, for as prophecy says: – Fill the pot, Eddy, supernaculum – a blazing star's a rare spectaculum. Go out both of you and look at the sun, I say, an' ye'll see the condition he's in – off!"

'Begad, sure enough, Jack gave a bounce to the door, and his wife leaped like a two-year-ould, till they were both got on a stile beside the house to see what was wrong in the sky.

'"Arrah, what is it, Jack," said she; "can you see anything?"

'"No," says he, "sorra the full o' my eye of anything I can spy, barrin' the sun himself, that's not visible in regard of the clouds, God guard us! I doubt there's something to happen."

174

THE PUDDING BEWITCHED

"'If there wasn't, Jack, what 'ud put Harry, that knows so much, in the state he's in?"

"'I doubt it's this marriage,' said Jack: 'betune ourselves, it's not over an' above religious for Moll to marry a black-mouth, an only for –; but it can't be helped now, though you see not a taste o' the sun is willin' to show his face upon it."

"As to that," says the wife, winkin' wid both her eyes, "if Gusty's satisfied wid Moll, it's enough. I know who'll carry the whip hand, anyhow; but in the manetime let us ax Harry 'ithin what ails the sun."

'Well, they accordianly went in an' put the question to him:

"'Harry, what's wrong, ahagur? What is it now, for if anybody alive knows, 'tis yourself?"

"'Ah!" said Harry, screwin' his mouth wid a kind of a dhry smile, "the sun has a hard twist o' the cholic; but never mind that, I tell you you'll have a merrier weddin' than you think, that's all;" and havin' said this, he put on his hat and left the house.

'Now, Harry's answer relieved them very much, and so, afther calling to him to be back for the dinner, Jack sat down to take a shough o' the pipe, and the wife lost no time in tying up the pudden and puttin' it in the pot to be boiled.

'In this way things went on well enough for a while, Jack smokin' away, an' the wife cookin' and dhressin' at the rate of a hunt. At last, Jack, while sittin', as I said, contentedly at the fire, thought he could persave an odd dancin' kind of motion in the pot that puzzled him a good deal.

"'Katty," said he, "what the dickens is in this pot on the fire?"

"'Nerra thing but the big pudden. Why do you ax?" says she.

"'Why," said he, "if ever a pot tuck it into its head to dance a jig, and this did. Thundher and sparbles, look at it!"

'Begad, it was thrue enough; there was the pot bobbin' up an' down and from side to side, jiggin' it away as merry as a grig; an' it was quite aisy to see that it wasn't the pot itself, but what was inside of it, that brought about the hornpipe.

"'Be the hole o' my coat," shouted Jack, "there's something alive in it, or it would never cut sich capers!"

THE MAGICAL FOLK OF IRELAND

'"Be gorra, there is, Jack; something sthrange entirely has got into it. Wirra, man alive, what's to be done?"

'Jist as she spoke, the pot seemed to cut the buckle in prime style, and afther a spring that 'ud shame a dancin'-masther, off flew the lid, and out bounced the pudden itself, hoppin', as nimble as a pea on a drum-head, about the floor. Jack blessed himself, and Katty crossed herself. Jack shouted, and Katty screamed. "In the name of goodness, keep your distance; no one here injured you!"

'The pudden, however, made a set at him, and Jack lepped first on a chair and then on the kitchen table to avoid it. It then danced towards Kitty, who was now repatin' her prayers at the top of her voice, while the cunnin' thief of a pudden was hoppin' and jiggin' it round her, as if it was amused at her distress.

'"If I could get the pitchfork," said Jack, "I'd dale wid it – by goxty I'd thry its mettle."

'"No, no," shouted Katty, thinkin' there was a fairy in it; "let us spake it fair. Who knows what harm it might do? Aisy now," said she to the pudden, "aisy, dear; don't harm honest people that never meant to offend you. It wasn't us – no, in troth, it was ould Harry Connolly that bewitched you; pursue *him* if you wish, but spare a woman like me; for, whisper, dear, I'm not in a condition to be frightened – troth I'm not."

'The pudden, bedad, seemed to take her at her word, and danced away from her towards Jack, who, like the wife, believin' there was a fairy in it, an' that spakin' it fair was the best plan, thought he would give it a soft word as well as her.

'"Plase your honour," said Jack, "she only spaiks the truth; an', upon my voracity, we both feels much oblaiged to your honour for your quietness. Faith, it's quite clear that if you weren't a gentlemanly pudden all out, you'd act otherwise. Ould Harry, the rogue, is your mark; he's jist gone down the road there, and if you go fast you'll overtake him. Be me song, your dancin' masther did his duty, anyhow. Thank your honour! God speed you, an may you never meet wid a parson or alderman in your thravels!"

'Jist as Jack spoke the pudden appeared to take the hint, for it quietly hopped out, and as the house was directly on the road-side, turned

THE PUDDING BEWITCHED

down towards the bridge, the very way that ould Harry went. It was very natural, of coorse, that Jack and Katty should go out to see how it intended to thravel; and, as the day was Sunday, it was but natural, too, that a greater number of people than usual were passin' the road. This was a fact; and when Jack and his wife were seen followin' the pudden, the whole neighbourhood was soon up and afther it.

"'Jack Rafferty, what is it? Katty, ahagur, will you tell us what it manes?"

"'Why," replied Katty, "it's my big pudden that's bewitched, an' it's now hot foot pursuin—;" here she stopped, not wishin' to mention her brother's name – "*some one* or other that surely put *pishrogues* an it."[2]

'This was enough; Jack, now seein' that he had assistance, found his courage comin' back to him; so says he to Katty, "Go home," says he, "an' lose no time in makin' another pudden as good, an' here's Paddy Scanlan's wife, Bridget, says she'll let you boil it on her fire, as you'll want our own to dress the rest o' the dinner: and Paddy himself will lend me a pitchfork, for purshuin to the morsel of that same pudden will escape till I let the wind out of it, now that I've the neighbours to back an' support me," says Jack.

'This was agreed to, and Katty went back to prepare a fresh pudden, while Jack an' half the townland pursued the other wid spades, graips, pitchforks, scythes, flails, and all possible description of instruments. On the pudden went, however, at the rate of about six Irish miles an hour, an' sich a chase never was seen. Catholics, Prodestants, an' Prosbytarians, were all afther it, armed, as I said, an' bad end to the thing but its own activity could save it. Here it made a hop, and there a prod was made at it; but off it went, an' some one, as eager to get a slice at it on the other side, got the prod instead of the pudden. Big Frank Farrell, the miller of Ballyboulteen, got a prod backwards that brought a hullabaloo out of him you might hear at the other end of the parish. One got a slice of a scythe, another a whack of a flail, a third a rap of a spade that made him look nine ways at wanst.

2 Put it under fairy influence.

THE MAGICAL FOLK OF IRELAND

"'Where is it goin'?" asked one. "My life for you, it's on it's way to Meeting. Three cheers for it if it turns to Carntaul." "Prod the sowl out of it, if it's a Prodestan'," shouted the others; "if it turns to the left, slice it into pancakes. We'll have no Prodestan' puddens here."

'Begad, by this time the people were on the point of beginnin' to have a regular fight about it, when, very fortunately, it took a short turn down a little by-lane that led towards the Methodist praichin-house, an' in an instant all parties were in an uproar against it as a Methodist pudden. "It's a Wesleyan," shouted several voices; "an' by this an' by that, into a Methodist chapel it won't put a foot today, or we'll lose a fall. Let the wind out of it. Come, boys, where's your pitchforks?"

'The divle purshuin to the one of them, however, ever could touch the pudden, an' jist when they thought they had it up against the gavel of the Methodist chapel, begad it gave them the slip, and hops over to the left, clane into the river, and sails away before all their eyes as light as an egg-shell.

'Now, it so happened that a little below this place, the demesne-wall of Colonel Bragshaw was built up to the very edge of the river on each side of its banks; and so findin' there was a stop put to their pursuit of it, they went home again, every man, woman and child of them, puzzled to think what the pudden was at all, what it meant, or where it was goin'! Had Jack Rafferty an' his wife been willin' to let out the opinion they held about Harry Connolly bewitchin' it, there is no doubt of it but poor Harry might be badly trated by the crowd, when their blood was up. They had sense enough, howandiver, to keep that to themselves, for Harry bein' an' ould bachelor, was a kind friend to the Raffertys. So, of coorse, there was all kinds of talk about it – some guessin' this, and some guessin' that – one party sayin' the pudden was of there side, another party denyin' it, an' insistin' it belonged to them, an' so on.

'In the manetime, Katty Rafferty, for 'fraid the dinner might come short, went home and made another pudden much about the same size as the one that had escaped, and bringin' it over to their next neighbour, Paddy Scanlan's, it was put into a pot and placed on the fire to boil, hopin' that it might be done in time, espishilly as they were to have the

THE PUDDING BEWITCHED

ministher, who loved a warm slice of a good pudden as well as e'er a gintleman in Europe.

'Anyhow, the day passed; Moll and Gusty were made man an' wife, an' no two could be more lovin'. Their friends that had been asked to the weddin' were saunterin' about in pleasant little groups till dinnertime, chattin' an' laughin'; but, above all things, sthrivin' to account for the figaries of the pudden; for, to tell the truth, its adventures had now gone through the whole parish.

'Well, at any rate, dinner-time was dhrawin' near, and Paddy Scanlan was sittin' comfortably wid his wife at the fire, the pudden boilen before their eyes, when in walks Harry Connolly, in a flutter, shoutin' – "Blood an' blunder-bushes, what are yez here for?"

"'Arra, why, Harry – why, avick?" said Mrs Scanlan.

"'Why," said Harry, "the sun's in the suds an' the moon in the high Horicks! Here's a clipstick comin' an, an' there you sit as unconsarned as if it was about to rain mether! Go out both of you, an' look at the sun, I say, and ye'll see the condition he's in – off!"

"'Ay, but, Harry, what's that rowled up in the tail of your cothamore[3] (big coat)?"

"'Out wid yez," said Harry, "an' pray aginst the dipstick – the sky's fallin'!"

'Begad, it was hard to say whether Paddy or the wife got out first, they were so much alarmed by Harry's wild thin face an' piercin' eyes; so out they went to see what was wondherful in the sky, an' kep' lookin' an' lookin' in every direction, but not a thing was to be seen, barrin' the sun shinin' down wid great good-humour, an' not a single cloud in the sky.

'Paddy an' the wife now came in laughin', to scould Harry, who, no doubt, was a great wag in his way when he wished. "Musha, bad scran to you, Harry –." They had time to say no more, howandiver, for, as they were goin' into the door, they met him comin' out of it wid a reek of smoke out of his tail like a lime-kiln.

3 Irish, *cóta mór.*

THE MAGICAL FOLK OF IRELAND

"'Harry,' shouted Bridget, "my sowl to glory, but the tail of your cothamore's a-fire – you'll be burned. Don't you see the smoke that's out of it?"

"'Cross yourselves three times," said Harry, widout stoppin', or even lookin' behind him, "for, as the prophecy says – Fill the pot, Eddy –". They could hear no more, for Harry appeared to feel like a man that carried something a great deal hotter than he wished, as anyone might see by the liveliness of his motions, and the quare faces he was forced to make as he went along.

"'What the dickens is he carryin' in the skirts of his big coat?" asked Paddy.

"'My sowl to happiness, but maybe he has stole the pudden," said Bridget, "for it's known that many a sthrange thing he does."

'They immediately examined the pot, but found that the pudden was there as safe as tuppence, an' this puzzled them the more, to think what it was he could be carryin' about wid him in the manner he did. But little they knew what he had done while they were sky-gazin!

'Well, anyhow, the day passed and the dinner was ready, an' no doubt but a fine gatherin' there was to partake of it. The Prosbytarian ministher met the Methodist praicher – a divilish stretcher of an appetite he had, in throth – on their way to Jack Rafferty's, an' as he knew he could take the liberty, why he insisted on his dinin' wid him; for, afther all, begad, in thim times the clargy of all descriptions lived upon the best footin' among one another, not all as one as now – but no matther. Well, they had nearly finished their dinner, when Jack Rafferty himself axed Katty for the pudden; but, jist as he spoke, in it came as big as a mess-pot.

"'Gintlemen," said he, "I hope none of you will refuse tastin' a bit of Katty's pudden: I don't mane the dancin' one that tuck to its thravels today, but a good solid fellow that she med since."

"'To be sure we won't," replied the priest; "so, Jack, put a thrifle on them three plates at your right hand, and send them over here to the clargy, an' maybe," he said, laughin' – for he was a droll good-humoured man – "maybe, Jack, we won't set you a proper example."

"'Wid a heart an' a half, yer reverence an' gintlemen; in throth, it's

THE PUDDING BEWITCHED

not a bad example ever any of you set us at the likes, or ever will set us, I'll go bail. An' sure I only wish it was betther fare I had for you; but we're humble people, gintlemen, and so you can't expect to meet here what you would in higher places."

"'Betther a male of herbs," said the Methodist praicher, "where pace is –." He had time to go no farther, however; for much to his amazement, the priest and the ministher started up from the table jist as he was goin' to swallow the first spoonful of the pudden, and before you could say Jack Robinson, started away at a lively jig down the floor.

'At this moment a neighbour's son came runnin' in, an' tould them that the parson was comin' to see the new-married couple, an' wish them all happiness; an' the words were scarcely out of his mouth when he made his appearance. What to think he knew not, when he saw the ministher footing it away at the rate of a weddin'. He had very little time, however, to think; for, before he could sit down, up starts the Methodist praicher, and clappin' his two fists in his sides chimes in in great style along wid him.

"'Jack Rafferty," says he – and, by the way, Jack was his tenant – "what the dickens does all this mane?" says he; "I'm amazed!"

"'The not a particle o' me can tell you," says Jack; "but will your reverence jist taste a morsel o' pudden, merely that the young couple may boast that you ait at their weddin'; for sure if *you* wouldn't, *who* would?"

"'Well," says he, "to gratify them I will; so just a morsel. But, Jack, this bates Bannagher," says he again, puttin' the spoonful o' pudden into his mouth; "has there been dhrink here?"

"'Oh, the divle a *spudh*," says Jack, "for although there's plinty in the house, faith, it appears the gintlemen wouldn't wait for it. Unless they tuck it elsewhere, I can make nothin' of this."

'He had scarcely spoken, when the parson, who was an active man, cut a caper a yard high, an' before you could bless yourself, the three clargy were hard at work dancin', as if for a wager. Begad, it would be unpossible for me to tell you the state the whole meetin' was in when they seen this. Some were hoarse wid laughin'; some turned up their

THE MAGICAL FOLK OF IRELAND

eyes wid wondher; many thought them mad, an' others thought they had turned up their little fingers a thrifle too often.

"'Be goxty, it's a burnin' shame," said one, "to see three black-mouth clargy in sich a state at this early hour!" "Thundher an' ounze, what's over them at all?" says others; "why, one would think they're bewitched. Holy Moses, look at the caper the Methodis cuts! An' as for the Recther, who would think he could handle his feet at such a rate! Be this an' be that, he cuts the buckle, and does the threblin' step aiquil to Paddy Horaghan, the dancin'-masther himself! An' see! Bad cess to the morsel of the parson that's not hard at *Peace upon a trancher*, an' it of a Sunday too! Whirroo, gintlemen, the fun's in yez afther all – whish I more power to yez!"

'The sorra's own fun they had, an' no wondher; but judge of what they felt, when all at once they saw ould Jack Rafferty himself bouncin' in among them, and footing it away like the best o' them. Bedad, no play could come up to it, an' nothin' could be heard but laughin', shouts of encouragement, and clappin' of hands like mad. Now the minute Jack Rallerty left the chair where he had been carvin' the pudden, ould Harry Connolly comes over and claps himself down in his place, in ordher to send it round, of coorse; an' he was scarcely sated, when who should make his appearance but Barney Hartigan, the piper. Barney, by the way, had been sent for early in the day, but bein' from home when the message for him went, he couldn't come any sooner.

"'Begorra," said Barney, "you're airly at the work, gintlemen! but what does this mane? But, divle may care, yez shan't want the music while there's a blast in the pipes, anyhow!" So sayin' he gave them *Jig Polthogue*, an' after that *Kiss my Lady*, in his best style.

'In the manetime the fun went on thick an' threefold, for it must be remembered that Harry, the ould knave, was at the pudden; an' maybe he didn't sarve it about in double quick time too. The first he helped was the bride, and, before you could say chopstick, she was at it hard an' fast before the Methodist praicher, who gave a jolly spring before her that threw them into convulsions. Harry liked this, and made up his mind soon to find partners for the rest; so he accordianly sent the pudden about like lightnin'; an' to make a long story short, barrin' the

182

THE PUDDING BEWITCHED

piper an' himself, there wasn't a pair o' heels in the house but was as busy at the dancin' as if their lives depinded on it.

"'Barney,' says Harry, "just taste a morsel o' this pudden; divle the such a bully of a pudden ever you ett; here, your sowl! thry a snig of it – it's beautiful."

"'To be sure I will," says Barney. "I'm not the boy to refuse a good thing; but, Harry, be quick, for you know my hands is engaged, an' it would be a thousand pities not to keep them in music, an' they so well inclined. Thank you, Harry; begad that is a famous pudden; but blood an' turnips, what's this for?"

'The word was scarcely out of his mouth when he bounced up, pipes an' all, an' dashed into the middle of the party. "Hurroo, your sowls, let us make a night of it! The Ballyboulteen boys for ever! Go it, your reverence – turn your partner – heel an' toe, ministher. Good! Well done again – Whish! Hurroo! Here's for Ballyboulteen, an' the sky over it!"

'Bad luck to the sich a set ever was seen together in this world, or will again, I suppose. The worst, however, wasn't come yet, for jist as they were in the very heat an' fury of the dance, what do you think comes hoppin' in among them but another pudden, as nimble an' merry as the first! That was enough; they all had heard of – the ministhers among the rest – an' most o' them had seen the other pudden, and knew that there must be a fairy in it, sure enough. Well, as I said, in it comes to the thick o' them; but the very appearance of it was enough. Off the three clargy danced, and off the whole wedders danced afther them, every one makin' the best of their way home; but not a sowl of them able to break out of the step, if they were to be hanged for it. Throth it wouldn't lave a laugh in you to see the parson dancin' down the road on his way home, and the ministher and Methodist praicher cuttin' the buckle as they went along in the opposite direction. To make short work of it, they all danced home at last, wid scarce a puff of wind in them; the bride and bridegroom danced away to bed; an' now, boys, come an' let us dance the *Horo Lheig* in the barn 'idout. But you see, boys, before we go, an' in ordher that I may make everything plain, I had as good tell you that Harry, in crossing the bridge of Ballyboulteen,

THE MAGICAL FOLK OF IRELAND

a couple of miles below Squire Bragshaw's demesne-wall, saw the pudden fioatin' down the river – the truth is he was waitin' for it , but be this as it may, he took it out, for the wather had made it as clane as a new pin, and tuckin' it up in the tail of his big coat, contrived, as you all guess, I suppose, to change it while Paddy Scanlan an' the wife were examinin' the sky; an' for the other, he contrived to bewitch it in the same manner, by getting' a fairy to go into it, for, indeed, it was purty well known that the same Harry was hand an' glove wid the *good people*. Others will tell you that it was half a pound of quicksilver he put into it; but that doesn't stand to raison. At any rate, boys, I have tould you the adventures of the Mad Pudden of Ballyboulteen; but I don't wish to tell you many other things about it that happened – *for fraid I'd tell a lie.*[4]

---

4 Some will insist that a fairy-man or fairy-woman has the power to bewitch a pudding by putting a fairy into it; whilst others maintain that a competent portion of quicksilver will make it dance over half the parish.

T'YEER-NA-N-OGE

There is a country called Tír-na-n-Og, which means the Country of the Young, for age and death have not found it; neither tears nor loud laughter have gone near it. The shadiest boskage covers it perpetually. One man has gone there and returned. The bard, Oisen, who wandered away on a white horse, moving on the surface of the foam with his fairy Niamh, lived there three hundred years, and then returned looking for his comrades. The moment his foot touched the earth his three hundred years fell on him, and he was bowed double, and his beard swept the ground. He described his sojourn in the Land of Youth to Patrick before he died. Since then many have seen it in many places; some in the depths of lakes, and have heard rising therefrom a vague sound of bells; more have seen it far off on the horizon, as they peered out from the western cliffs. Not three years ago a fisherman imagined that he saw it. It never appears unless to announce some national trouble.

There are many kindred beliefs. A Dutch pilot, settled in Dublin, told M. De La Boullage Le Cong, who travelled in Ireland in 1614, that round the poles were many islands; some hard to be approached because of the witches who inhabit them and destroy by storms those who seek to land. He had once, off the coast of Greenland, in sixty-one degrees of latitude, seen and approached such an island only to see it vanish. Sailing in an opposite direction, they met with the same island, and sailing near, were almost destroyed by a furious tempest.

According to many stories, Tír-na-n-Og is the favourite dwelling of the fairies. Some say it is triple – the island of the living, the island of victories and an underwater land.

THE LEGEND OF O'DONOGHUE[1]

T. Crofton Croker

In an age so distant that the precise period is unknown, a chieftain named O'Donoghue ruled over the country which surrounds the romantic Lough Lean, now called the lake of Killarney. Wisdom, beneficence, and justice distinguished his reign, and the prosperity and happiness of his subjects were their natural results. He is said to have been as renowned for his warlike exploits as for his pacific virtues; and as a proof that his domestic administration was not the less rigorous because it was mild, a rocky island is pointed out to strangers, called 'O'Donoghue's Prison', in which this prince once confined his own son for some act of disorder and disobedience.

His end – for it cannot correctly be called his death – was singular and mysterious. At one of those splendid feasts for which his court was celebrated, surrounded by the most distinguished of his subjects, he was engaged in a prophetic relation of the events which were to happen in ages yet to come. His auditors listened, now wrapt in wonder, now fired with indignation, burning with shame, or melted into sorrow, as he faithfully detailed the heroism, the injuries, the crimes, and the miseries of their descendants. In the midst of his predictions he rose slowly from his seat, advanced with a solemn, measured and majestic tread to the shore of the lake, and walked forward composedly upon its unyielding surface. When he had nearly reached the centre he paused for a moment, then, turning slowly round, looked toward his friends, and waving his arms to them with the cheerful air of one taking a short farewell, disappeared from their view.

---

1 *Fairy Legends of the South of Ireland.*

THE LEGEND OF O'DONOGHUE

The memory of the good O'Donoghue has been cherished by successive generations with affectionate reverence; and it is believed that at sunrise, on every May-day morning, the anniversary of his departure, he revisits his ancient domains: a favoured few only are in general permitted to see him, and this distinction is always an omen of good fortune to the beholders; when it is granted to many it is a sure token of an abundant harvest, – a blessing, the want of which during this prince's reign was never felt by his people.

Some years have elapsed since the last appearance of O'Donoghue. The April of that year had been remarkably wild and stormy; but on May-morning the fury of the elements had altogether subsided. The air was hushed and still; and the sky, which was reflected in the serene lake, resembled a beautiful but deceitful countenance, whose smiles, after the most tempestuous emotions, tempt the stranger to believe that it belongs to a soul which no passion has ever ruffled.

The first beams of the rising sun were just gilding the lofty summit of Glenaa, when the waters near the eastern shore of the lake became suddenly and violently agitated, though all the rest of its surface lay smooth and still as a tomb of polished marble; the next morning a foaming wave darted forward, and, like a proud high-crested war-horse, exulting in his strength, rushed across the lake toward Toomies mountain. Behind this wave appeared a stately warrior fully armed, mounted upon a milk-white steed; his snowy plume waved gracefully from a helmet of polished steel, and at his back fluttered a light blue scarf. The horse, apparently exulting in his noble burden, sprung after the wave along the water, which bore him up like firm earth, while showers of spray that glittered brightly in the morning sun were dashed up at every bound.

The warrior was O'Donoghue; he was followed by numberless youths and maidens, who moved lightly and unconstrained over the watery plain, as the moonlight fairies glide through the fields of air; they were linked together by garlands of delicious spring flowers, and they timed their movements to strains of enchanting melody. When O'Donoghue had nearly reached the western side of the lake, he suddenly turned his steed, and directed his course along the wood-

THE MAGICAL FOLK OF IRELAND

fringed shore of Glenaa, preceded by the huge wave that curled and foamed up as high as the horse's neck, whose fiery nostrils snorted above it. The long train of attendants followed with playful deviations the track of their leader, and moved on with unabated fleetness to their celestial music, till gradually, as they entered the narrow strait between Glenaa and Dinis, they became involved in the mists which still partially floated over the lakes, and faded from the view of the wondering beholders: but the sound of their music still fell upon the ear, and echo, catching up the harmonious strains, fondly repeated and prolonged them in soft and softer tones, till the last faint repetition died away, and the hearers awoke as from a dream of bliss.

RENT-DAY

'Oh, ullagone! ullagone! this is a wide world, but what will we do in it, or where will we go?' muttered Bill Doody, as he sat on a rock by the Lake of Killarney. 'What will we do? Tomorrow's rent-day, and Tim the Driver swears if we don't pay our rent, he'll cant every ha'perth we have; and then, sure enough, there's Judy and myself, and the poor grawls,[1] will be turned out to starve on the high-road, for the never a halfpenny of rent have I! – Oh hone, that ever I should live to see this day!'

Thus did Bill Doody bemoan his hard fate, pouring his sorrows to the reckless waves of the most beautiful of lakes, which seemed to mock his misery as they rejoiced beneath the cloudless sky of a May morning. That lake, glittering in sunshine, sprinkled with fairy isles of rock and verdure, and bounded by giant hills of ever-varying hues, might, with its magic beauty, charm all sadness but despair; for alas,

> 'How ill the scene that offers rest
> And heart that cannot rest agree!'

Yet Bill Doody was not so desolate as he supposed; there was one listening to him he little thought of, and help was at hand from a quarter he could not have expected.

'What's the matter with you, my poor man?' said a tall, portly-looking gentleman, at the same time stepping out of a furze-brake. Now Bill was seated on a rock that commanded the view of a large field. Nothing in the field could be concealed from him, except this

1 Children.

THE MAGICAL FOLK OF IRELAND

furze-brake, which grew in a hollow near the margin of the lake. He was, therefore, not a little surprised at the gentleman's sudden appearance, and began to question whether the personage before him belonged to this world or not. He, however, soon mustered courage sufficient to tell him how his crops had failed, how some bad member had charmed away his butter, and how Tim the Driver threatened to turn him out of the farm if he didn't pay up every penny of the rent by twelve o'clock next day.

'A sad story, indeed,' said the stranger; 'but surely, if you represented the case to your landlord's agent, he won't have the heart to turn you out.'

'Heart, your honour; where would an agent get a heart!' exclaimed Bill. 'I see your honour does not know him; besides, he has an eye on the farm this long time for a fosterer of his own; so I expect no mercy at all at all, only to be turned out.'

'Take this, my poor fellow, take this,' said the stranger, pouring a purse full of gold into Bill's old hat, which in his grief he had flung on the ground. 'Pay the fellow your rent, but I'll take care it shall do him no good. I remember the time when things went otherwise in this country, when I would have hung up such a fellow in the twinkling of an eye!'

These words were lost upon Bill, who was insensible to everything but the sight of the gold, and before he could unfix his gaze, and lift up his head to pour out his hundred thousand blessings, the stranger was gone. The bewildered peasant looked around in search of his benefactor, and at last he thought he saw him riding on a white horse a long way off on the lake.

'O'Donoghue, O'Donoghue!' shouted Bill; 'the good, the blessed O'Donoghue!' and he ran capering like a madman to show Judy the gold, and to rejoice her heart with the prospect of wealth and happiness.

The next day Bill proceeded to the agent's; not sneakingly, with his hat in his hand, his eyes fixed on the ground, and his knees bending under him; but bold and upright, like a man conscious of his independence.

'Why don't you take off your hat, fellow? Don't you know you are speaking to a magistrate?' said the agent.

RENT-DAY

'I know I'm not speaking to the king, sir,' said Bill; 'and I never takes off my hat but to them I can respect and love. The Eye that sees all knows I've no right either to respect or love an agent!'

'You scoundrel!' retorted the man in office, biting his lips with rage at such an unusual and unexpected opposition, 'I'll teach you how to be insolent again; I have the power, remember.'

'To the cost of the country, I know you have,' said Bill, who still remained with his head as firmly covered as if he was the Lord Kingsale himself.

'But, come,' said the magistrate; 'have you got the money for me? this is rent-day. If there's one penny of it wanting, or the running gale that's due, prepare to turn out before night, for you shall not remain another hour in possession.'

'There is your rent,' said Bill, with an unmoved expression of tone and countenance; 'you'd better count it, and give me a receipt in full for the running gale and all.'

The agent gave a look of amazement at the gold; for it was gold – real guineas! and not bits of dirty ragged small notes, that are only fit to light one's pipe with. However willing the agent may have been to ruin, as he thought, the unfortunate tenant, he took up the gold, and handed the receipt to Bill, who strutted off with it as proud as a cat of her whiskers.

The agent going to his desk shortly after, was confounded at beholding a heap of gingerbread cakes instead of the money he had deposited there. He raved and swore, but all to no purpose; the gold had become gingerbread cakes, just marked like the guineas, with the king's head; and Bill had the receipt in his pocket; so he saw there was no use in saying anything about the affair, as he would only get laughed at for his pains.

From that hour Bill Doody grew rich; all his undertakings prospered; and he often blesses the day that he met with O'Donoghue, the great prince that lives down under the lake of Killarney.

LOUGHLEAGH
(LAKE OF HEALING)[1]

'Do you see that bit of a lake,' said my companion, turning his eyes towards the acclivity that overhung Loughleagh. 'Troth, and as little as you think of it, and as ugly as it looks with its weeds and its flags, it is the most famous one in all Ireland. Young and ould, rich and poor, far and near, have come to that lake to get cured of all kinds of scurvy and sores. The Lord keep us our limbs whole and sound, for it's a sorrowful thing not to have the use o' them. 'Twas but last week we had a great grand Frenchman here; and, though he came upon crutches, faith he went home sound as a bell; and well he paid Billy Reily for curing him.'

'And, pray, how did Billy Reily cure him?'

'Oh, well enough. He took his long pole, dipped it down to the bottom of the lake, and brought up on the top of it as much plaster as would do for a thousand sores!'

'What kind of plaster?'

'What kind of plaster? why, black plaster to be sure; for isn't the bottom of the lake filled with a kind of black mud which cures all the world?'

'Then it ought to be a famous lake indeed.'

'Famous, and so it is,' replied my companion, 'but it isn't for its cures neather that it is famous; for, sure, doesn't all the world know there is a fine beautiful city at the bottom of it, where the good people live just like Christians. Troth, it is the truth I tell you; for *Shemus-a-sneidh* saw it all when he followed his dun cow that was stolen.'

1 *Dublin and London Magazine*, 1825.

LOUGHLEAGH

'Who stole her?'

'I'll tell you all about it: – Shemus was a poor gossoon, who lived on the brow of the hill, in a cabin with his ould mother. They lived by hook and by crook, one way and another, in the best way they could. They had a bit of ground that gave 'em the preaty, and a little dun cow that gave 'em the drop o' milk; and, considering how times go, they weren't badly off, for Shemus was a handy gossoon to boot; and, while minden the cow, cut heath and made brooms, which his mother sould on a market-day, and brought home the bit o' tobaccy, the grain of salt, and other nic-nackenes, which a poor body can't well do widout. Once upon a time, however, Shemus went farther than usual up the mountain, looken for long heath, for town's-people don't like to stoop, and so like long handles to their brooms. The little dun cow was a'most as cunning as a Christian sinner, and followed Shemus like a lap-dog everywhere he'd go, so that she required little or no herden. On this day she found nice picken on a round spot as green as a leek; and, as poor Shemus was weary, as a body would be on a fine summer's day, he lay down on the grass to rest himself, just as we're resten ourselves on the cairn here. Begad, he hadn't long lain there, sure enough, when, what should he see but whole loads of ganconers[2] dancing about the place. Some o' them were hurlen, some kicking a football, and others leaping a kick-step-and-a-lep. They were so soople and so active that Shemus was highly delighted with the sport, and a little tanned-skinned chap in a red cap pleased him better than any o' them, bekase he used to tumble the other fellows like mushrooms. At one time he had kept the ball up for as good as half-an-hour, when Shemus cried out, "Well done, my hurler!" The word wasn't well out of his mouth when whap went the ball on his eye, and flash went the fire. Poor Shemus thought he was blind, and roared out, "Mille murdher!"[3] but the only thing he heard was a loud laugh. "Cross o' Christ about us," says he to himself, "what

---

2 Ir. *gean-canach* – i.e., love-talker, a kind of fairy appearing in lonesome valleys, a dudeen (tobacco-pipe) in his mouth, making love to milk-maids, etc.

3 A thousand murders.

THE MAGICAL FOLK OF IRELAND

is this for?" and afther rubbing his eyes they came to a little, and he could see the sun and the sky, and, by-and-by, he could see everything but his cow and the mischievous ganconers. They were gone to their rath or mote; but where was the little dun cow? He looked, and he looked, and he might have looked from that day to this, bekase she wasn't to be found, and good reason why – the ganconers took her away with 'em.

'Shemus-a-sneidh, however, didn't think so, but ran home to his mother.

'"Where is the cow, Shemus?" axed the ould woman.

'"Och, musha, bad luck to her," said Shemus, "I donna where she is!"

'"Is that an answer, you big blaggard, for the likes o' you to give your poor ould mother?" said she.

'"Och, musha," said Shemus, "don't kick up saich a *bollhous* about nothing. The ould cow is safe enough, I'll be bail, some place or other, though I could find her if I put my eyes upon *kippeens*,[4] and, speaking of eyes, faith, I had very good luck o' my side, or I had naver a one to look after her."

'"Why, what happened your eyes, agrah?" axed the ould woman.

'"Oh! Didn't the ganconers – the Lord save us from all hurt and harm! – drive their hurlen ball into them both! and sure I was stone blind for an hour."

'"And may be," said the mother, "the good people took our cow?"

'"No, nor the devil a one of them," said Shemus, "for, by the powers, that same cow is as knowen as a lawyer, and wouldn't be such a fool as to go with the ganconers while she could get such grass as I found for her today."

In this way, continued my informant, they talked about the cow all that night, and next mornen both o' them set off to look for her. After searching every place, high and low, what should Shemus see sticking

---

4 Ir. *cipin* – i.e., a stick, a twig.

194

LOUGHLEAGH

out of a bog-hole but something very like the horns of his little beast!

'Oh, mother, mother,' said he, 'I've found her!'

'Where, alanna?' axed the ould woman.

'In the bog-hole, mother,' answered Shemus.

At this the poor ould creathure set up such a *pullallue* that she brought the seven parishes about her; and the neighbours soon pulled the cow out of the bog-hole. You'd swear it was the same, and yet it wasn't, as you shall hear by-and-by.

Shemus and his mother brought the dead beast home with them; and, after skinnen her, hung the meat up in the chimney. The loss of the drop o' milk was a sorrowful thing, and though they had a good deal of meat, that couldn't last always; besides, the whole parish *faughed* upon them for eating the flesh of a beast that died without bleeden. But the pretty thing was, they couldn't eat the meat after all, for when it was boiled it was as tough as carrion, and as black as a turf. You might as well think of sinking your teeth in an oak plank as into a piece of it, and then you'd want to sit a great piece from the wall for fear of knocking your head against it when pulling it through your teeth. At last and at long run they were forced to throw it to the dogs, but the dogs wouldn't smell to it, and so it was thrown into the ditch, where it rotted. This misfortune cost poor Shemus many a salt tear, for he was now obliged to work twice as hard as before, and be out cutten heath on the mountain late and early. One day he was passing by this cairn with a load of brooms on his back, when what should he see but the little dun cow and two red-headed fellows herding her.

'That's my mother's cow,' said Shemus-a-sneidh.

'No, it is not,' said one of the chaps.

'But I say it is,' said Shemus, throwing the brooms on the ground, and seizing the cow by the horns. At that the red fellows drove her as fast as they could to this steep place, and with one leap she bounced over, with Shemus stuck fast to her horns. They made only one splash in the lough, when the waters closed over 'em, and they sunk to the bottom. Just as Shemus-a-sneidh thought that all was over with him, he found himself before a most elegant palace built with jewels, and

THE MAGICAL FOLK OF IRELAND

all manner of fine stones. Though his eyes were dazzled with the splendour of the place, faith he had gomsh[5] enough not to let go his holt, but in spite of all they could do, he held his little cow by the horns. He was axed into the palace, but wouldn't go.

The hubbub at last grew so great that the door flew open, and out walked a hundred ladies and gentlemen, as fine as any in the land.

'What does this boy want?' axed one o' them, who seemed to be the masther.

'I want my mother's cow,' said Shemus.

'That's not your mother's cow,' said the gentleman.

'Bethershin!'[6] cried Shemus-a-sneid; 'don't I know her as well as I know my right hand?'

'Where did you lose her?' axed the gentleman. And so Shemus up and tould him all about it: how he was on the mountain – how he saw the good people hurlen – how the ball was knocked in his eye, and his cow was lost.

'I believe you are right,' said the gentleman, pulling out his purse, 'and here is the price of twenty cows for you.'

'No, no,' said Shemus, 'you'll not catch ould buds wid chaff. I'll have my cow and nothen else.'

'You're a funny fellow,' said the gentleman; 'stop here and live in a palace.'

'I'd rather live with my mother.'

'Foolish boy!' said the gentleman; 'stop here and live in a palace.'

'I'd rather live in my mother's cabin.'

'Here you can walk through gardens loaded with fruit and flowers.'

'I'd rather,' said Shemus, 'be cutting heath on the mountain.'

'Here you can eat and drink of the best.'

'Since I've got my cow, I can have milk once more with the praties.'

'Oh!' cried the ladies, gathering round him, 'sure you wouldn't take away the cow that gives us milk for our tea?'

5 Otherwise 'gumshun' – i.e., sense, cuteness.

6 Ir. *B'éidir sin* – i.e. 'that is possible'.

LOUGHLEAGH

'Oh!' said Shemus, 'my mother wants milk as bad as anyone, and she must have it; so there is no use in your palaver – I must have my cow.'

At this they all gathered about him and offered him bushels of gould, but he wouldn't have anything but his cow. Seeing him as obstinate as a mule, they began to thump and beat him; but still he held fast by the horns, till at length a great blast of wind blew him out of the place, and in a moment he found himself and the cow standing on the side of the lake, the water of which looked as if it hadn't been disturbed since Adam was a boy – and that's a long time since.

Well, Shemus-a-sneidh drove home his cow, and right glad his mother was to see her; but the moment she said 'God bless the beast,' she sunk down like the *breesha*[7] of a turf rick. That was the end of Shemus-a-sneidh's dun cow.

'And, sure,' continued my companion, standing up, 'it is now time for me to look after my brown cow, and God send the ganconers haven't taken her!'

Of this I assured him there could be no fear; and so we parted.

---

7 Ir. *briseadh* – i.e., breaking.

THE PHANTOM ISLE

Giraldus Cambrensis[1]

Among the other islands is one newly formed, which they call the Phantom Isle, which had its origin in this manner. One calm day a large mass of earth rose to the surface of the sea, where no land had ever been seen before, to the great amazement of islanders who observed it. Some of them said that it was a whale, or other immense sea-monster; others, remarking that it continued motionless, said, 'No; it is land.' In order, therefore, to reduce their doubts to certainty, some picked young men of the island determined to approach nearer the spot in a boat. When, however, they came so near to it that they thought they should go on shore, the island sank in the water and entirely vanished from sight. The next day it re-appeared, and again mocked the same youths with the like delusion. At length, on their rowing towards it on the third day, they followed the advice of an older man, and let fly an arrow, barbed with red-hot steel, against the island; and then landing, found it stationary and habitable.

This adds one to the many proofs that fire is the greatest of enemies to every sort of phantom; in so much that those who have seen apparitions, fall into a swoon as soon as they are sensible of the brightness of fire. For fire, both from its position and nature, is the noblest of the elements, being a witness of the secrets of the heavens.

The sky is fiery; the planets are fiery; the bush burnt with fire, but was not consumed; the Holy Ghost sat upon the apostles in tongues of fire.

---

1 'Giraldus Cambrensis' was born in 1146, and wrote a celebrated account of Ireland.

GIANTS

When the pagan gods of Ireland – the *Tuath-De-Danān* – robbed of worship and offerings, grew smaller and smaller in the popular imagination, until they turned into the fairies, the pagan heroes grew bigger and bigger, until they turned into the giants.

THE GIANT'S STAIRS[1]

T. Crofton Croker

On the road between Passage and Cork there is an old mansion called Ronayne's Court. It may be easily known from the stack of chimneys and the gable-ends, which are to be seen, look at it which way you will. Here it was that Maurice Ronayne and his wife Margaret Gould kept house, as may be learned to this day from the great old chimney-piece, on which is carved their arms. They were a mighty worthy couple, and had but one son, who was called Philip, after no less a person than the King of Spain.

Immediately on his smelling the cold air of this world the child sneezed, which was naturally taken to be a good sign of his having a clear head; and the subsequent rapidity of his learning was truly amazing, for on the very first day a primer was put into his hands he tore out the A, B, C page and destroyed it, as a thing quite beneath his notice. No wonder, then, that both father and mother were proud of their heir, who gave such indisputable proofs of genius, or, as they called it in that part of the world, '*genus*'.

One morning, however, Master Phil, who was then just seven years old, was missing, and no one could tell what had become of him: servants were sent in all directions to seek him, on horseback and on foot, but they returned without any tidings of the boy, whose disappearance altogether was most unaccountable. A large reward was offered, but it produced them no intelligence, and years rolled away without Mr and Mrs Ronayne having obtained any satisfactory account of the fate of their lost child.

---

1 *Fairy Legends of the South of Ireland.*

THE GIANT'S STAIRS

There lived at this time, near Carrigaline, one Robert Kelly, a blacksmith by trade. He was what is termed a handy man, and his abilities were held in much estimation by the lads and the lasses of the neighbourhood; for, independent of shoeing horses, which he did to great perfection, and making plough-irons, he interpreted dreams for the young women, sung 'Arthur O'Bradley' at their weddings, and was so good-natured a fellow at a christening, that he was gossip to half the country round.

Now it happened that Robin had a dream himself, and young Philip Ronayne appeared to him in it, at the dead hour of the night. Robin thought he saw the boy mounted upon a beautiful white horse, and that he told him how he was made a page to the giant Mahon MacMahon, who had carried him off, and who held his court in the hard heart of the rock. 'The seven years – my time of service – are clean out, Robin,' said he, 'and if you release me this night I will be the making of you for ever after.'

'And how will I know,' said Robin – cunning enough, even in his sleep – 'but this is all a dream?'

'Take that,' said the boy, 'for a token' – and at the word the white horse struck out with one of his hind legs, and gave poor Robin such a kick in the forehead that, thinking he was a dead man, he roared as loud as he could after his brains, and woke up, calling a thousand murders. He found himself in bed, but he had the mark of the blow, the regular print of a horse-shoe, upon his forehead as red as blood; and Robin Kelly, who never before found himself puzzled at the dream of any other person, did not know what to think of his own.

Robin was well acquainted with the Giant's Stairs – as, indeed, who is not that knows the harbour? They consist of great masses of rock, which, piled one above another, rise like a flight of steps from very deep water, against the bold cliff of Carrigmahon. Nor are they badly suited for stairs to those who have legs of sufficient length to stride over a moderate-sized house, or to enable them to clear the space of a mile in a hop, step and jump. Both these feats the giant MacMahon was said to have performed in the days of Finnian glory; and the common tradition of the country placed his dwelling within the cliff up whose side the stairs led.

THE MAGICAL FOLK OF IRELAND

Such was the impression which the dream made on Robin, that he determined to put its truth to the test. It occurred to him, however, before setting out on this adventure, that a plough-iron may be no bad companion, as, from experience, he knew it was an excellent knock-down argument, having on more occasions than one settled a little disagreement very quietly: so, putting one on his shoulder, off he marched, in the cool of the evening, through Glaun a Thowk (the Hawk's Glen) to Monkstown. Here an old gossip of his (Tom Clancey by name) lived, who, on hearing Robin's dream, promised him the use of his skiff, and, moreover, offered to assist in rowing it to the Giant's Stairs.

After a supper, which was of the best, they embarked. It was a beautiful still night, and the little boat glided swiftly along. The regular dip of the oars, the distant song of the sailor, and sometimes the voice of a belated traveller at the ferry of Carrigaloe, alone broke the quietness of the land and sea and sky. The tide was in their favour, and in a few minutes Robin and his gossip rested on their oars under the dark shadow of the Giant's Stairs. Robin looked anxiously for the entrance to the Giant's palace, which, it was said, may be found by any one seeking it at midnight; but no such entrance could he see. His impatience had hurried him there before that time, and after waiting a considerable space in a state of suspense not to be described, Robin, with pure vexation, could not help exclaiming to his companion, ''Tis a pair of fools we are, Tom Clancey, for coming here at all on the strength of a dream.'

'And whose doing is it,' said Tom, 'but your own?'

At the moment he spoke they perceived a faint glimmering of light to proceed from the cliff, which gradually increased until a porch big enough for a king's palace unfolded itself almost on a level with the water. They pulled the skiff directly towards the opening, and Robin Kelly, seizing his plough-iron, boldly entered with a strong hand and a stout heart. Wild and strange was that entrance, the whole of which appeared formed of grim and grotesque faces, blending so strangely each with the other that it was impossible to define any: the chin of one formed the nose of another; what appeared to be a fixed and stern eye, if dwelt upon, changed to a gaping mouth; and the lines of the

THE GIANT'S STAIRS

lofty forehead grew into a majestic and flowing beard. The more Robin allowed himself to contemplate the forms around him, the more terrific they became; and the stoney expression of this crowd of faces assumed a savage ferocity as his imagination converted feature after feature into a different shape and character. Losing the twilight in which these indefinite forms were visible, he advanced through a dark and devious passage, whilst a deep and rumbling noise sounded as if the rock was about to close upon him, and swallow him up alive for ever. Now, indeed, poor Robin felt afraid.

'Robin, Robin,' said he, 'if you were a fool for coming here, what in the name of fortune are you now?' But, as before, he had scarcely spoken, when he saw a small light twinkling through the darkness of the distance, like a star in the midnight sky. To retreat was out of the question; for so many turnings and windings were in the passage, that he considered he had but little chance of making his way back. He, therefore, proceeded towards the bit of light, and came at last into a spacious chamber, from the roof of which hung the solitary lamp that had guided him. Emerging from such profound gloom, the single lamp afforded Robin abundant light to discover several gigantic figures seated round a massive stone table, as if in serious deliberation, but no word disturbed the breathless silence which prevailed. At the head of this table sat Mahon MacMahon himself, whose majestic beard had taken root, and in the course of ages grown into the stone slab. He was the first who perceived Robin; and instantly starting up, drew his long beard from out the huge piece of rock in such haste and with so sudden a jerk that it was shattered into a thousand pieces.

'What seek you?' he demanded in a voice of thunder.

'I come,' answered Robin, with as much boldness as he could put on, for his heart was almost fainting within him; 'I come,' said he, 'to claim Philip Ronayne, whose time of service is out this night.'

'And who sent you here?' said the giant.

''Twas of my own accord I came,' said Robin.

'Then you must single him out from among my pages,' said the giant; 'and if you fix on the wrong one, your life is the forfeit. Follow me.' He led Robin into a hall of vast extent, and filled with lights; along

THE MAGICAL FOLK OF IRELAND

either side of which were rows of beautiful children, all apparently seven years old, and none beyond that age, dressed in green, and every one exactly dressed alike.

'Here,' said Mahon, 'you are free to take Philip Ronayne, if you will; but, remember, I give but one choice.'

Robin was sadly perplexed; for there were hundreds upon hundreds of children; and he had no very clear recollection of the boy he sought. But he walked along the hall, by the side of Mahon, as if nothing was the matter, although his great iron dress clanked fearfully at every step, sounding louder than Robin's own sledge battering on his anvil.

They had nearly reached the end without speaking, when Robin, seeing that the only means he had was to make friends with the giant, determined to try what effect a few soft words might have.

''Tis a fine wholesome appearance the poor children carry,' remarked Robin, 'although they have been here so long shut out from the fresh air and the blessed light of heaven. 'Tis tenderly your honour must have reared them!'

'Ay,' said the giant, 'that is true for you; so give me your hand; for you are, I believe, a very honest fellow for a blacksmith.'

Robin at the first look did not much like the huge size of the hand, and, therefore, presented his plough-iron, which the giant seizing, twisted in his grasp round and round again as if it had been a potato stalk. On seeing this all the children set up a shout of laughter. In the midst of their mirth Robin thought he heard his name called; and all ear and eye, he put his hand on the boy who he fancied had spoken, crying out at the same time, 'Let me live or die for it, but this is young Phil Ronayne.'

'It is Philip Ronayne – happy Philip Ronayne,' said his young companions; and in an instant the hall became dark. Crashing noises were heard, and all was in strange confusion; but Robin held fast his prize, and found himself lying in the grey dawn of the morning at the head of the Giant's Stairs with the boy clasped in his arms.

Robin had plenty of gossips to spread the story of his wonderlul adventure: Passage, Monkstown, Carrigaline – the whole barony of Kerricurrihy rung with it.

THE GIANT'S STAIRS

'Are you quite sure, Robin, it is young Phil Ronayne you have brought back with you?' was the regular question; for although the boy had been seven years away, his appearance now was just the same as on the day he was missed. He had neither grown taller nor older in look, and he spoke of things which had happened before he was carried off as one awakened from sleep, or as if they had occurred yesterday.

'Am I sure? Well, that's a queer question,' was Robin's reply; 'seeing the boy has the blue eye of the mother, with the foxy hair of the father; to say nothing of the *purty* wart on the right side of his little nose.'

However Robin Kelly may have been questioned, the worthy couple of Ronayne's Court doubted not that he was the deliverer of their child from the power of the giant MacMahon; and the reward they bestowed on him equalled their gratitude.

Philip Ronayne lived to be an old man; and he was remarkable to the day of his death for his skill in working brass and iron, which it was believed he had learned during his seven years' apprenticeship to the giant Mahon MacMahon.

A LEGEND OF KNOCKMANY

William Carleton

What Irish man, woman, or child has not heard of our renowned Hibernian Hercules, the great and glorious Fin M'Coul? Not one, from Cape Clear to the Giant's Causeway, nor from that back again to Cape Clear. And, by-the-way, speaking of the Giant's Causeway brings me at once to the beginning of my story. Well, it so happened that Fin and his gigantic relatives were all working at the Causeway, in order to make a bridge, or what was still better, a good stout pad-road, across to Scotland; when Fin, who was very fond of his wife Oonagh, took it into his head that he would go home and see how the poor woman got on in his absence. To be sure, Fin was a true Irishman, and so the sorrow thing in life brought him back, only to see that she was snug and comfortable, and, above all things, that she got her rest well at night; for he knew that the poor woman, when he was with her, used to be subject to nightly qualms and configurations, that kept him very anxious, decent man, striving to keep her up to the good spirits and health that she had when they were first married. So, accordingly, he pulled up a fir-tree, and, after lopping off the roots and branches, made a walking-stick of it, and set out on his way to Oonagh.

Oonagh, or rather Fin, lived at this time on the very tip-top of Knockmany Hill, which faces a cousin of its own called Cullamore, that rises up, half-hill, half-mountain, on the opposite side – east-east by south, as the sailors say, when they wish to puzzle a landsman.

Now, the truth is, for it must come out, that honest Fin's affection for his wife, though cordial enough in itself, was by no manner of means the real cause of his journey home. There was at that time another giant, named Cucullin – some say he was Irish, and some say he was Scotch – but whether Scotch or Irish, sorrow doubt of it but he was a

A LEGEND OF KNOCKMANY

targer. No other giant of the day could stand before him; and such was his strength, that, when well vexed, he could give a stamp that shook the country about him. The fame and name of him went far and near; and nothing in the shape of a man, it was said, had any chance with him in a fight. Whether the story is true or not, I cannot say, but the report went that, by one blow of his fists he flattened a thunderbolt, and kept it in his pocket, in the shape of a pancake, to show to all his enemies, when they were about to fight him. Undoubtedly he had given every giant in Ireland a considerable beating, barring Fin M'Coul himself; and he swore, by the solemn contents of Moll Kelly's Primer, that he would never rest, night or day, winter or summer, till he would serve Fin with the same sauce, if he could catch him. Fin, however, who no doubt was the cock of the walk on his own dunghill, had a strong disinclination to meet a giant who could make a young earthquake, or flatten a thunderbolt when he was angry; so he accordingly kept dodging about from place to place, not much to his credit as a Trojan, to be sure, whenever he happened to get the hard word that Cucullin was on the scent of him. This, then, was the marrow of the whole movement, although he put it on his anxiety to see Oonagh; and I am not saying but there was some truth in that too. However, the short and long of it was, with reverence be it spoken, that he heard Cucullin was coming to the Causeway to have a trial of strength with him; and he was naturally enough seized, in consequence, with a very warm and sudden sit of affection for his wife, poor woman, who was delicate in her health, and leading, besides, a very lonely, uncomfortable life of it (he assured them) in his absence. He accordingly pulled up the fir-tree, as I said before, and having snedded it into a walking-stick, set out on his affectionate travels to see his darling Oonagh on the top of Knockmany, by the way.

In truth, to state the suspicions of the country at the time, the people wondered very much why it was that Fin selected such a windy spot for his dwelling-house, and they even went so far as to tell him as much.

'What can you mane, Mr M'Coul,' said they, 'by pitching your tent upon the top of Knockmany, where you never are without a breeze, day or night, winter or summer, and where you're often forced to take your

THE MAGICAL FOLK OF IRELAND

nightcap[1] without either going to bed or turning up your little finger; ay, an' where, besides this, there's the sorrow's own want of water?'

'Why,' said Fin, 'ever since I was the height of a round tower, I was known to be fond of having a good prospect of my own; and where the dickens, neighbours, could I find a better spot for a good prospect than the top of Knockmany? As for water, I am sinking a pump,[2] and, plase goodness, as soon as the Causeway's made, I intend to finish it.'

Now, this was more of Fin's philosophy; for the real state of the case was, that he pitched upon the top of Knockmany in order that he might be able to see Cucullin coming towards the house, and, of course, that he himself might go to look after his distant transactions in other parts of the country, rather than – but no matter – we do not wish to be too hard on Fin. All we have to say is, that if he wanted a spot from which to keep a sharp look-out – and, between ourselves, he did want it grievously – barring Slieve Croob, or Slieve Donard, or its own cousin, Cullamore, he could not find a neater or more convenient situation for it in the sweet and sagacious province of Ulster.

'God save all here!' said Fin, good-humouredly, on putting his honest face into his own door.

'Musha, Fin, avick, an' you're welcome home to your own Oonagh, you darlin' bully.' Here followed a smack that is said to have made the waters of the lake at the bottom of the hill curl, as it were, with kindness and sympathy.

'Faith,' said Fin, 'beautiful; an' how are you, Oonagh – and how did you sport your figure during my absence, my bilberry?'

'Never a merrier – as bouncing a grass widow as ever there was in sweet "Tyrone among the bushes".'

Fin gave a short, good-humoured cough, and laughed most heartily, to show her how much he was delighted that she made herself happy in his absence.

---

1 A common name for the cloud or rack that hangs, as a forerunner of wet weather, about the peak of a mountain.

2 There is upon the top of this hill an opening that bears a very strong resemblance to the crater of an extinct volcano.

A LEGEND OF KNOCKMANY

'An' what brought you home so soon, Fin?' said she.

'Why, avourneen,' said Fin, putting in his answer in the proper way, 'never the thing but the purest of love and affection for yourself. Sure you know that's truth, anyhow, Oonagh.'

Fin spent two or three happy days with Oonagh, and felt himself very comfortable, considering the dread he had of Cucullin. This, however, grew upon him so much that his wife could not but perceive something lay on his mind which he kept altogether to himself. Let a woman alone, in the meantime, for ferreting or wheedling a secret out of her good man, when she wishes. Fin was a proof of this.

'It's this Cucullin,' said he, 'that's troubling me. When the fellow gets angry, and begins to stamp, he'll shake you a whole townland; and it's well known that he can stop a thunderbolt, for he always carries one about him in the shape of a pancake, to show to anyone that might misdoubt it.'

As he spoke, he clapped his thumb in his mouth, which he always did when he wanted to prophesy, or to know anything that happened in his absence; and the wife, who knew what he did it for, said, very sweetly,

'Fin, darling, I hope you don't bite your thumb at me, dear?'

'No,' said Fin; 'but I bite my thumb, acushla,' said he.

'Yes, jewel; but take care and don't draw blood,' said she. 'Ah, Fin! Don't, my bully – don't.'

'He's coming,' said Fin; 'I see him below Dungannon.'

'Thank goodness, dear! An' who is it, avick? Glory be to God!'

'That baste, Cucullin,' replied Fin; 'and how to manage I don't know. If I run away, I am disgraced; and I know that sooner or later I must meet him, for my thumb tells me so.'

'When will he be here?' said she.

'Tomorrow, about two o'clock,' replied Fin, with a groan.

'Well, my bully, don't be cast down,' said Oonagh; 'depend on me, and maybe I'll bring you better out of this scrape than ever you could bring yourself, by your rule o' thumb.'

This quieted Fin's heart very much, for he knew that Oonagh was hand and glove with the fairies; and, indeed, to tell the truth, she was

THE MAGICAL FOLK OF IRELAND

supposed to be a fairy herself. If she was, however, she must have been a kind-hearted one, for, by all accounts, she never did anything but good in the neighbourhood.

Now it so happened that Oonagh had a sister named Granua, living opposite them, on the very top of Cullamore, which I have mentioned already, and this Granua was quite as powerful as herself. The beautiful valley that lies between them is not more than about three or four miles broad, so that of a summer's evening, Granua and Oonagh were able to hold many an agreeable conversation across it, from the one hill-top to the other. Upon this occasion Oonagh resolved to consult her sister as to what was best to be done in the difficulty that surrounded them.

'Granua,' said she, 'are you at home?'

'No,' said the other; 'I'm picking bilberries in Althadhawan' (*Anglicé*, the Devil's Glen).

'Well,' said Oonagh, 'get up to the top of Cullamore, look about you, and then tell us what you see.'

'Very well,' replied Granua; after a few minutes, 'I am there now.'

'What do you see?' asked the other.

'Goodness be about us!' exclaimed Granua, 'I see the biggest giant that ever was known coming up from Dungannon.'

'Ay,' said Oonagh, 'there's our difficulty. That giant is the great Cucullin; and he's now commin' up to leather Fin. What's to be done?'

'I'll call to him,' she replied, 'to come up to Cullamore and refresh himself, and maybe that will give you and Fin time to think of some plan to get yourselves out of the scrape. But,' she proceeded, 'I'm short of butter, having in the house only half-a-dozen firkins, and as I'm to have a few giants and giantesses to spend the evenin' with me, I'd feel thankful, Oonagh, if you'd throw me up fifteen or sixteen tubs, or the largest miscaun you have got, and you'll oblige me very much.'

'I'll do that with a heart and a-half,' replied Oonagh; 'and, indeed, Granua, I feel myself under great obligations to you for your kindness in keeping him off of us till we see what can be done; for what would become of us all if anything happened to Fin, poor man.'

She accordingly got the largest miscaun of butter she had – which might be about the weight of a couple a dozen mill-stones, so that you

A LEGEND OF KNOCKMANY

may easily judge of its size – and calling up to her sister, 'Granua,' said she, 'are you ready? I'm going to throw you up a miscaun, so be prepared to catch it.'

'I will,' said the other; 'a good throw now, and take care it does not fall short.'

Oonagh threw it; but, in consequence of her anxiety about Fin and Cucullin, she forgot to say the charm that was to send it up, so that, instead of reaching Cullamore, as she expected, it fell about half-way between the two hills, at the edge of the Broad Bog near Augher.

'My curse upon you!' she exclaimed; 'you've disgraced me. I now change you into a grey stone. Lie there as a testimony of what has happened; and may evil betide the first living man that will ever attempt to remove or injure you!'

And, sure enough, there it lies to this day, with the mark of the four fingers and thumb imprinted in it, exactly as it came out of her hand.

'Never mind,' said Granua, 'I must only do the best I can with Cucullin. If all fail, I'll give him a cast of heather broth to keep the wind out of his stomach, or a panada of oak-bark to draw it in a bit; but, above all things, think of some plan to get Fin out of the scrape he's in, otherwise he's a lost man. You know you used to be sharp and ready-witted; and my own opinion, Oonagh, is, that it will go hard with you, or you'll outdo Cucullin yet.'

She then made a high smoke on the top of the hill, after which she put her finger in her mouth, and gave three whistles, and by that Cucullin knew he was invited to Cullamore – for this was the way that the Irish long ago gave a sign to all strangers and travellers, to let them know they were welcome to come and take share of whatever was going.

In the meantime, Fin was very melancholy, and did not know what to do, or how to act at all. Cucullin was an ugly customer, no doubt, to meet with; and, moreover, the idea of the confounded 'cake' aforesaid flattened the very heart within him. What chance could he have, strong and brave though he was, with a man who could, when put in a passion, walk the country into earthquakes and knock thunderbolts into pancakes? The thing was impossible; and Fin knew not on what

211

THE MAGICAL FOLK OF IRELAND

hand to turn him. Right or left – backward or forward – where to go he could form no guess whatsoever.

'Oonagh,' said he, 'can you do nothing for me? Where's all your invention? Am I to be skivered like a rabbit before your eyes, and to have my name disgraced forever in the sight of all my tribe, and me the best man among them? How am I to fight this man-mountain – this huge cross between an earthquake and a thunder-bolt? – with a pancake in his pocket that was once –'

'Be easy, Fin,' replied Oonagh; 'troth, I'm ashamed of you. Keep your toe in your pump, will you? Talking of pancakes, maybe we'll give him as good as any he brings with him – thunderbolt or otherwise. If I don''t treat him to as smart feeding as he's got this many a day, never trust Oonagh again. Leave him to me, and do just as I bid you.'

This relieved Fin very much; for, after all, he had great confidence in his wife, knowing, as he did, that she had got him out of many a quandary before. The present, however, was the greatest of all; but still he began to get courage, and was able to eat his victuals as usual. Oonagh then drew the nine woollen threads of different colours, which she always did to find out the best way of succeeding in anything of importance she went about. She then plaited them into three plaits with three colours in each, putting one on her right arm, one round her heart, and the third round her right ankle, for then she knew that nothing could fail with her that she undertook.

Having everything now prepared, she sent round to the neighbours and borrowed one-and-twenty iron griddles, which she took and kneaded into the hearts of one-and-twenty cakes of bread, and these she baked on the fire in the usual way, setting them aside in the cupboard according as they were done. She then put down a large pot of new milk, which she made into curds and whey, and gave Fin due instructions how to use the curds when Cucullin should come. Having done all this, she sat down quite contented, waiting for his arrival on the next day about two o'clock, that being the hour at which he was expected – for Fin knew as much by the sucking of his thumb. Now, this was a curious property that Fin's thumb had; but, notwithstanding all the wisdom and logic he used to suck out of it, it could never have stood to him here

A LEGEND OF KNOCKMANY

were it not for the wit of his wife. In this very thing, moreover, he was very much resembled by his great foe, Cucullin; for it was well known that the huge strength he possessed all lay in the middle finger of his right hand, and that, if he happened by any mischance to lose it, he was no more, notwithstanding his bulk, than a common man.

At length, the next day, he was seen coming across the valley, and Oonagh knew that it was time to commence operations. She immediately made the cradle, and desired Fin to lie down in it, and cover himself up with the clothes.

'You must pass for your own child,' said she; 'so just lie there snug, and say nothing, but be guided by me.' This, to be sure, was wormwood to Fin – I mean going into the cradle in such a cowardly manner – but he knew Oonagh well; and finding that he had nothing else for it, with a very rueful face he gathered himself into it, and lay snug, as she had desired him.

About two o'clock, as he had been expected, Cucullin came in. 'God save all here!' said he; 'is this where the great Fin M'Coul lives?'

'Indeed it is, honest man,' replied Oonagh; 'God save you kindly – won't you be sitting?'

'Thank you, ma'am,' says he, sitting down; 'you're Mrs M'Coul, I suppose?'

'I am,' said she; 'and I have no reason, I hope, to be ashamed of my husband.'

'No,' said the other, 'he has the name of being the strongest and bravest man in Ireland; but for all that, there's a man not far from you that's very desirous of taking a shake with him. Is he at home?'

'Why, then, no,' she replied; 'and if ever a man left his house in a fury, he did. It appears that some one told him of a big basthoon of a giant called Cucullin being down at the Causeway to look for him, and so he set out there to try if he could catch him. Troth, I hope, for the poor giant's sake, he won't meet with him, for if he does, Fin will make paste of him at once.'

'Well,' said the other, 'I am Cucullin, and I have been seeking him these twelve months, but he always kept clear of me; and I will never rest night or day till I lay my hands on him.'

213

THE MAGICAL FOLK OF IRELAND

At this Oonagh set up a loud laugh, of great contempt, by-the-way, and looked at him as if he was only a mere handful of a man.

'Did you ever see Fin?' said she, changing her manner all at once.

'How could I?' said he; 'he always took care to keep his distance.'

'I thought so,' she replied; 'I judged as much; and if you take my advice, you poor-looking creature, you'll pray night and day that you may never see him, for I tell you it will be a black day for you when you do. But, in the meantime, you perceive that the wind's on the door, and as Fin himself is from home, maybe you'd be civil enough to turn the house, for it's always what Fin does when he's here.'

This was a startler even to Cucullin; but he got up, however, and after pulling the middle finger of his right hand until it cracked three times, he went outside, and getting his arms about the house, completely turned it as she had wished. When Fin saw this, he felt a certain description of moisture, which shall be nameless, oozing out through every pore of his skin; but Oonagh, depending upon her woman's wit, felt not a whit daunted.

'Arrah, then,' said she, 'as you are so civil, maybe you'd do another obliging turn for us, as Fin's not here to do it himself. You see, after this long stretch of dry weather we've had, we feel very badly off for want of water. Now, Fin says there's a fine spring-well somewhere under the rocks behind the hill here below, and it was his intention to pull them asunder; but having heard of you, he left the place in such a fury, that he never thought of it. Now, if you try to find it, troth I'd feel it a kindness.'

She then brought Cucullin down to see the place, which was then all one solid rock; and, after looking at it for some time, he cracked his right middle finger nine times, and, stooping down, tore a cleft about four hundred feet deep, and a quarter of a mile in length, which has since been christened by the name of Lumford's Glen. This feat nearly threw Oonagh herself off her guard; but what won't a woman's sagacity and presence of mind accomplish?

'You'll now come in,' said she, 'and eat a bit of such humble fare as we can give you. Fin, even although he and you are enemies, would scorn not to treat you kindly in his own house; and, indeed, if

A LEGEND OF KNOCKMANY

I didn't do it even in his absence, he would not be pleased with me.'

She accordingly brought him in, and placing half-a-dozen of the cakes we spoke of before him, together with a can or two of butter, a side of boiled bacon, and a stack of cabbage, she desired him to help himself – for this, be it known, was long before the invention of potatoes. Cucullin, who, by the way, was a glutton as well as a hero, put one of the cakes in his mouth to take a huge whack out of it, when both Fin and Oonagh were stunned with a noise that resembled something between a growl and a yell. 'Blood and fury!' he shouted; 'how is this? Here are two of my teeth out! What kind of bread is this you gave me?'

'What's the matter?' said Oonagh coolly.

'Matter!' shouted the other again; 'why, here are the two best teeth in my head gone.'

'Why,' said she, 'that's Fin's bread – the only bread he ever eats when at home; but, indeed, I forgot to tell you that nobody can eat it but himself, and that child in the cradle there. I thought, however, that, as you were reported to be rather a stout little fellow of your size, you might be able to manage it, and I did not wish to affront a man that thinks himself able to fight Fin. Here's another cake – maybe it's not so hard as that.'

Cucullin at the moment was not only hungry, but ravenous, so he accordingly made a fresh set at the second cake, and immediately another yell was heard twice as loud as the first. 'Thunder and giblets!' he roared, 'take your bread out of this, or I will not have a tooth in my head; there's another pair of them gone!'

'Well, honest man,' replied Oonagh, 'if you're not able to eat the bread, say so quietly, and don't be wakening the child in the cradle there. There, now, he's awake upon me.'

Fin now gave a skirl that startled the giant, as coming from such a youngster as he was represented to be. 'Mother,' said he, 'I'm hungry – get me something to eat.' Oonagh went over, and putting into his hand a cake *that had no griddle in it*, Fin, whose appetite in the meantime was sharpened by what he saw going forward, soon made it disappear. Cucullin was thunderstruck, and secretly thanked his stars that he had the good fortune to miss meeting Fin, for, as he said to himself, I'd

THE MAGICAL FOLK OF IRELAND

have no chance with a man who could eat such bread as that, which even his son that's but in his cradle can munch before my eyes.

'I'd like to take a glimpse at the lad in the cradle,' said he to Oonagh; 'for I can tell you that the infant who can manage that nutriment is no joke to look at, or to feed of a scarce summer.'

'With all the veins of my heart,' rephed Oonagh; 'get up, acushla, and show this decent little man something that won't be unworthy of your father, Fin M'Coul.'

Fin, who was dressed for the occasion as much like a boy as possible, got up, and bringing Cucullin out, 'Are you strong?' said he.

'Thunder an' ounds!' exclaimed the other, 'what a voice in so small a chap!'

'Are you strong?' said Fin again; 'are you able to squeeze water out of that white stone?' he asked, putting one into Cucullin's hand. The latter squeezed and squeezed the stone, but to no purpose; he might pull the rocks of Lumford's Glen asunder, and flatten a thunderbolt, but to squeeze water out of a white stone was beyond his strength. Fin eyed him with great contempt, as he kept straining and squeezing and squeezing and straining, till he got black in the face with the efforts.

'All, you're a poor creature!' said Fin. 'You a giant! Give me the stone here, and when I'll show what Fin's little son can do, you may then judge of what my daddy himself is.'

Fin then took the stone, and slyly exchanging it for the curds, he squeezed the latter until the whey, as clear as water, oozed out in a little shower from his hand.

'I'll now go in,' said he 'to my cradle; for I scorn to lose my time with any one that's not able to eat my daddy's bread, or squeeze water out of a stone. Bedad, you had better be off out of this before he comes back; for if he catches you, it's in flummery he'd have you in two minutes.'

Cucullin, seeing what he had seen, was of the same opinion himself; his knees knocked together with the terror of Fin's return, and he accordingly hastened in to bid Oonagh farewell, and to assure her, that from that day out, he never wished to hear of, much less to see, her husband. 'I admit fairly that I'm not a match for him,' said he, 'strong

216

A LEGEND OF KNOCKMANY

as I am; tell him I will avoid him as I would the plague, and that I will make myself scarce in this part of the country while I live.'

Fin, in the meantime, had gone into the cradle, where he lay very quietly, his heart at his mouth with delight that Cucullin was about to take his departure, without discovering the tricks that had been played off on him.

'It's well for you,' said Oonagh, 'that he doesn't happen to be here, for it's nothing but hawk's meat he'd make of you.'

'I know that,' says Cucullin; 'divil a thing else he'd make of me; but before I go, will you let me feel what kind of teeth they are that can eat griddle-bread hke that?' – and he pointed to it as he spoke.

'With all pleasure in life,' said she; 'only, as they're far back in his head, you must put your finger a good way in.'

Cucullin was surprised to find such a powerful set of grinders in one so young; but he was still much more so on finding, when he took his hand from Fin's mouth, that he had left the very finger upon which his whole strength depended, behind him. He gave one loud groan, and fell down at once with terror and weakness. This was all Fin wanted, who now knew that his most powerful and bitterest enemy was completely at his mercy. He instantly started out of the cradle, and in a few minutes the great Cucullin, that was for such a length of time the terror of him and all his followers, lay a corpse before him. Thus did Fin, through the wit and invention of Oonagh, his wife, succeed in overcoming his enemy by stratagem, which he never could have done by force: and thus also is it proved that the women, if they bring us *into* many an unpleasant scrape, can sometimes succeed in getting us *out of* others that are as bad.

KINGS, QUEENS, PRINCESSES, EARLS, ROBBERS

THE TWELVE WILD GEESE[1]

Patrick Kennedy

There was once a King and Queen that lived very happily together, and they had twelve sons and not a single daughter. We are always wishing for what we haven't, and don't care for what we have, and so it was with the Queen. One day in winter, when the bawn was covered with snow, she was looking out of the parlour window, and saw there a calf that was just killed by the butcher, and a raven standing near it. 'Oh,' says she, 'if I had only a daughter with her skin as white as that snow, her cheeks as red as that blood, and her hair as black as that raven, I'd give away every one of my twelve sons for her.' The moment she said the word, she got a great fright, and a shiver went through her, and in an instant after, a severe-looking old woman stood before her. 'That was a wicked wish you made,' said she, 'and to punish you it will be granted. You will have such a daughter as you desire, but the very

1 *The Fireside Stories of Ireland* (Gill & Son, Dublin).

THE TWELVE WILD GEESE

day of her birth you will lose your other children.' She vanished the moment she said the words.

And that very way it turned out. When she expected her delivery, she had her children all in a large room of the palace, with guards all round it, but the very hour her daughter came into the world, the guards inside and outside heard a great whirling and whistling, and the twelve princes were seen flying one after another out through the open window, and away like so many arrows over the woods. Well, the king was in great grief for the loss of his sons, and he would be very enraged with his wife if he only knew that she was so much to blame for it.

Everyone called the little princess Snow-white-and-Rose-red on account of her beautiful complexion. She was the most loving and lovable child that could be seen anywhere. When she was twelve years old she began to be very sad and lonely, and to torment her mother, asking her about her brothers that she thought were dead, for none up to that time ever told her the exact thing that happened to them. The secret was weighing very heavy on the Queen's conscience, and as the little girl persevered in her questions, at last she told her. 'Well, mother,' said she, 'it was on my account my poor brothers were changed into wild geese, and are now suffering all sorts of hardship: before the world is a day older, I'll be off to seek them, and try to restore them to their own shapes.'

The King and Queen had her well watched, but all was no use. Next night she was getting through the woods that surrounded the palace, and she went on and on that night, and till the evening of next day. She had a few cakes with her, and she got nuts, and *mugoreens* (fruit of the sweet briar), and some sweet crabs, as she went along. At last she came to a nice wooden house just at sunset. There was a fine garden round it, full of the handsomest flowers, and a gate in the hedge. She went in, and saw a table laid out with twelve plates, and twelve knives and forks, and twelve spoons, and there were cakes, and cold wild fowl, and fruit along with the plates, and there was a good fire, and in another long room there were twelve beds. Well, while she was looking about her she heard the gate opening, and footsteps along the walk, and in came twelve young men, and there was great grief

219

THE MAGICAL FOLK OF IRELAND

and surprise on all their faces when they laid eyes on her. 'Oh, what misfortune sent you here?' said the eldest. 'For the sake of a girl we were obliged to leave our father's court, and be in the shape of wild geese all day. That's twelve years ago, and we took a solemn oath that we would kill the first young girl that came into our hands. It's a pity to put such an innocent and handsome girl as you are out of the world, but we must keep our oath.' 'But,' said she, 'I'm your only sister, that never knew anything about this till yesterday; and I stole away from our father's and mother's palace last night to find you out and relieve you if I can.' Every one of them clasped his hands, and looked down on the floor, and you could hear a pin fall till the eldest cried out, 'A curse light on our oath! what shall we do?' 'I'll tell you that,' said an old woman that appeared at the instant among them. 'Break your wicked oath, which no one should keep. If you attempted to lay an uncivil finger on her I'd change you into twelve *booliaun buis* (stalks of ragweed), but I wish well to you as well as to her. She is appointed to be your deliverer in this way. She must spin and knit twelve shirts for you out of bog-down, to be gathered by her own hands on the moor just outside of the wood. It will take her five years to do it, and if she once speaks, or laughs, or cries the whole time, you will have to remain wild geese by day till you're called out of the world. So take care of your sister; it is worth your while.' The fairy then vanished, and it was only a strife with the brothers to see who would be first to kiss and hug their sister.

So for three long years the poor young princess was occupied pulling bog-down, spinning it, and knitting it into shirts, and at the end of the three years she had eight made. During all that time, she never spoke a word, nor laughed, nor cried: the last was the hardest to refrain firom. One fine day she was sitting in the garden spinning, when in sprung a fine greyhound and bounded up to her, and laid his paws on her shoulder, and licked her forehead and her hair. The next minute a beautiful young prince rode up to the little garden gate, took off his hat, and asked for leave to come in. She gave him a little nod, and in he walked. He made ever so many apologies for intruding, and asked her ever so many questions, but not a word could he get out of her. He

THE TWELVE WILD GEESE

loved her so much from the first moment, that he could not leave her till he told her he was king of a country just bordering on the forest, and he begged her to come home with him, and be his wife. She couldn't help loving him as much as he did her, and though she shook her head very often, and was very sorry to leave her brothers, at last she nodded her head, and put her hand in his. She knew well enough that the good fairy and her brothers would be able to find her out. Before she went she brought out a basket holding all her bog-down, and another holding the eight shirts. The attendants took charge of these, and the prince placed her before him on his horse. The only thing that disturbed him while riding along was the displeasure his stepmother would feel at what he had done. However, he was full master at home, and as soon as he arrived he sent for the bishop, got his bride nicely dressed, and the marriage was celebrated, the bride answering by signs. He knew by her manners she was of high birth, and no two could be fonder of each other.

The wicked stepmother did all she could to make mischief, saying she was sure she was only a woodman's daughter; but nothing could disturb the young king's opinion of his wife. In good time the young queen was delivered of a beautiful boy, and the king was so glad he hardly knew what to do for joy. All the grandeur of the christening and the happiness of the parents tormented the bad woman more than I can tell you, and she determined to put a stop to all their comfort. She got a sleeping posset given to the young mother, and while she was thinking and thinking how she could best make away with the child, she saw a wicked-looking wolf in the garden, looking up at her, and licking his chops. She lost no time, but snatched the child from thie arms of the sleeping woman, and pitched it out. The beast caught it in his mouth, and was over the garden fence in a minute. The wicked woman then pricked her own fingers, and dabbled the blood round the mouth of the sleeping mother.

Well, the young king was just then coming into the big bawn from hunting, and as soon as he entered the house, she beckoned to him, shed a few crocodile tears, began to cry and wring her hands, and hurried him along the passage to the bedchamber.

THE MAGICAL FOLK OF IRELAND

Oh, wasn't the poor king frightened when he saw the queen's mouth bloody, and missed his child? It would take two hours to tell you the devilment of the old queen, the confusion and fright, and grief of the young king and queen, the bad opinion he began to feel of his wife, and the struggle she had to keep down her bitter sorrow, and not give way to it by speaking or lamenting. The young king would not allow any one to be called, and ordered his step-mother to give out that the child fell from the mother's arms at the window, and that a wild beast ran off with it. The wicked woman pretended to do so, but she told underhand to everybody she spoke to what the king and herself saw in the bed-chamber.

The young queen was the most unhappy woman in the three kingdoms for a long time, between sorrow for her child, and her husband's bad opinion; still she neither spoke nor cried, and she gathered bog-down and went on with the shirts. Often the twelve wild geese would be seen lighting on the trees in the park or on the smooth sod, and looking in at her windows. So she worked on to get the shirts finished, but another year was at an end, and she had the twelfth shirt finished except one arm, when she was obliged to take to her bed, and a beautiful girl was born.

Now the king was on his guard, and he would not let the mother and child be left alone for a minute; but the wicked woman bribed some of the attendants, set others asleep, gave the sleepy posset to the queen, and had a person watching to snatch the child away, and kill it. But what should she see but the same wolf in the garden looking up and licking his chops again? Out went the child, and away with it flew the wolf, and she smeared the sleeping mother's mouth and face with blood, and then roared, and bawled, and cried out to the king and to everybody she met, and the room was filled, and everyone was sure the young queen had just devoured her own babe.

The poor mother thought now her life would leave her. She was in such a state she could neither think nor pray, but she sat like a stone, and worked away at the arm of the twelfth shirt.

The king was for taking her to the house in the wood where he found her, but the stepmother, and the lords of the court, and the judges

THE TWELVE WILD GEESE

would not hear of it, and she was condemned to be burned in the big bawn at three o'clock the same day. When the hour drew near, the king went to the farthest part of his palace, and there was no more unhappy man in his kingdom at that hour.

When the executioners came and led her off, she took the pile of shirts in her arms. There were still a few stitches wanted, and while they were tying her to the stakes she still worked on. At the last stitch she seemed overcome and dropped a tear on her work, but the moment after she sprang up, and shouted out, 'I am innocent; call my husband!' The executioners stayed their hands, except one wicked-disposed creature, who set fire to the faggot next him, and while all were struck in amaze, there was a rushing of wings, and in a moment the twelve wild geese were standing around the pile. Before you could count twelve, she flung a shirt over each bird, and there in the twinkling of an eye were twelve of the finest young men that could be collected out of a thousand. While some were untying their sister, the eldest, taking a strong stake in his hand, struck the busy executioner such a blow that he never needed another.

While they were comforting the young queen, and the king was hurrying to the spot, a fine-looking woman appeared among them holding the babe on one arm and the little prince by the hand. There was nothing but crying for joy, and laughing for joy, and hugging and kissing, and when any one had time to thank the good fairy, who in the shape of a wolf, carried the child away, she was not to be found. Never was such happiness enjoyed in any palace that ever was built, and if the wicked queen and her helpers were not torn by wild horses, they richly deserved it.

THE LAZY BEAUTY AND HER AUNTS

Patrick Kennedy

There was once a poor widow woman, who had a daughter that was as handsome as the day, and as lazy as a pig, saving your presence. The poor mother was the most industrious person in the townland, and was a particularly good hand at the spinning-wheel. It was the wish of her heart that her daughter should be as handy as herself; but she'd get up late, eat her breakfast before she'd finish her prayers, and then go about dawdling, and anything she handled seemed to be burning her fingers. She drawled her words as if it was a great trouble to her to speak, or as if her tongue was as lazy as her body. Many a heart-scald her poor mother got with her, and still she was only improving like dead fowl in August.

Well, one morning that things were as bad as they could be, and the poor woman was giving tongue at the rate of a mill-clapper, who should be riding by but the king's son. 'Oh dear, oh dear, good woman!' said he, 'you must have a very bad child to make you scold so terribly. Sure it can't be this handsome girl that vexed you!' 'Oh, please your Majesty, not at all,' says the old dissembler. 'I was only checking her for working herself too much. Would your Majesty believe it? She spins three pounds of flax in a day, weaves it into linen the next, and makes it all into shirts the day after.' 'My gracious,' says the prince, 'she's the very lady that will just fill my mother's eye, and herself's the greatest spinner in the kingdom. Will you put on your daughter's bonnet and cloak, if you please, ma'am, and set her behind me? Why, my mother will be so delighted with her, that perhaps she'll make her her daughter-in-law in a week, that is, if the young woman herself is agreeable.'

1 *Fireside Stories of Ireland.*

THE LAZY BEAUTY AND HER AUNTS

Well, between the confusion, and the joy, and the fear of being found out, the women didn't know what to do; and before they could make up their minds, young Anty (Anastasia) was set behind the prince, and away he and his attendants went, and a good heavy purse was left behind with the mother. She pulllillued a long time after all was gone, in dread of something bad happening to the poor girl.

The prince couldn't judge of the girl's breeding or wit from the few answers he pulled out of her. The queen was struck in a heap when she saw a young country girl sitting behind her son, but when she saw her handsome face, and heard all she could do, she didn't think she could make too much of her. The prince took an opportunity of whispering her that if she didn't object to be his wife she must strive to please his mother. Well, the evening went by, and the prince and Anty were getting fonder and fonder of one another, but the thought of the spinning used to send the cold to her heart every moment. When bed-time came, the old queen went along with her to a beautiful bedroom, and when she was bidding her good-night, she pointed to a heap of fine flax, and said, 'You may begin as soon as you like tomorrow morning, and I'll expect to see these three pounds in nice thread the morning after.' Little did the poor girl sleep that night. She kept crying and lamenting that she didn't mind her mother's advice better. When she was left alone next morning, she began with a heavy heart; and though she had a nice mahogany wheel and the finest flax you ever saw, the thread was breaking every moment. One while it was as fine as a cobweb, and the next as coarse as a little boy's whipcord. At last she pushed her chair back, let her hands fall in her lap, and burst out a-crying.

A small, old woman with surprising big feet appeared before her at the same moment, and said, 'What ails you, you handsome colleen?' 'An' haven't I all that flax to spin before tomorrow morning, and I'll never be able to have even five yards of fine thread of it put together.' 'An' would you think bad to ask poor Colliagh Cushmōr (Old woman Big-foot) to your wedding with the young prince? If you promise me that, all your three pounds will be made into the finest of thread while you're taking your sleep tonight.' 'Indeed, you must be there and welcome, and I'll honour you all the days of your life.' 'Very well;

THE MAGICAL FOLK OF IRELAND

stay in your room till tea-time, and tell the queen she may come in for her thread as early as she likes tomorrow morning.' It was all as she said; and the thread was finer and evener than the gut you see with fly-fishers. 'My brave girl you were!' says the queen. 'I'll get my own mahogany loom brought in to you, but you needn't do anything more today. Work and rest, work and rest, is my motto. Tomorrow you'll weave all this thread, and who knows what may happen?'

The poor girl was more frightened this time than the last, and she was so afraid to lose the prince. She didn't even know how to put the warp in the gears, nor how to use the shuttle, and she was sitting in the greatest grief, when a little woman, who was mighty well-shouldered about the hips, all at once appeared to her, told her her name was *Colliagh Cromanmōr*, and made the same bargain with her as Colliagh Cushmōr. Great was the queen's pleasure when she found early in the morning a web as fine and white as the finest paper you ever saw. 'The darling you were!' says she. 'Take your ease with the ladies and gentlemen today, and if you have all this made into nice shirts tomorrow you may present one of them to my son, and be married to him out of hand.'

Oh, wouldn't you pity poor Anty the next day, she was now so near the prince, and, maybe, would be soon so far from him. But she waited as patiently as she could with scissors, needle and thread in hand, till a minute after noon. Then she was rejoiced to see the third old woman appear. She had a big red nose, and informed Anty that people called her *Shron Mor Rua* on that account. She was up to her as good as the others, for a dozen fine shirts were lying on the table when the queen paid her an early visit.

Now there was nothing talked of but the wedding, and I needn't tell you it was grand. The poor mother was there along with the rest, and at the dinner the old queen could talk of nothing but the lovely shirts, and how happy herself and the bride would be after the honeymoon, spinning, and weaving, and sewing shirts and shifts without end. The bridegroom didn't like the discourse, and the bride liked it less, and he was going to say something, when the footman came up to the head of the table and said to the bride, 'Your ladyship's aunt, Colliagh Cushmōr, bade me ask might she come in.' The bride blushed and wished she was seven miles under the floor, but well became the prince. 'Tell Mrs

THE LAZY BEAUTY AND HER AUNTS

Cushmōr,' said he, 'that any relation of my bride's will be always heartily welcome wherever she and I are.' In came the woman with the big foot, and got a seat near the prince. The old queen didn't like it much, and after a few words she asked rather spitefully, 'Dear ma'am, what's the reason your foot is so big?' '*Musha*, faith, your majesty, I was standing almost all my life at the spinning-wheel, and that's the reason.' 'I declare to you, my darling,' said the prince, 'I'll never allow you to spend one hour at the same spinning-wheel.' The same footman said again, 'Your ladyship's aunt, Colliach Cromanmōr, wishes to come in, if the genteels and yourself have no objection.' Very *sharoose* (displeased) was Princess Anty, but the prince sent her welcome, and she took her seat, and drank healths apiece to the company. 'May I ask, ma'am?' says the old queen, 'why you're so wide half-way between the head and the feet?' 'That, your majesty, is owing to sitting all my life at the loom.' 'By my sceptre,' says the prince, 'my wife shall never sit there an hour.' The footman again came up. 'Your ladyship's aunt, Colliach Shron Mor Rua, is asking leave to come into the banquet.' More blushing on the bride's face, but the bridegroom spoke out cordially, 'Tell Mrs Shron Mor Rua she's doing us an honour.' In came the old woman, and great respect she got near the top of the table, but the people down low put up their tumblers and glasses to their noses to hide the grins. 'Ma'am,' says the old queen, 'will you tell us, if you please, why your nose is so big and red?' 'Throth, your majesty, my head was bent down over the stitching all my life, and all the blood in my body ran into my nose.' 'My darling,' said the prince to Anty, 'if ever I see a needle in your hand, I'll run a hundred miles from you.'

'And in troth, girls and boys, though it's a diverting story, I don't think the moral is good; and if any of you *thuckeens* go about imitating Anty in her laziness, you'll find it won't thrive with you as it did with her. She was beautiful beyond compare, which none of you are, and she had three powerful fairies to help her besides. There's no fairies now, and no prince or lord to ride by, and catch you idling or working; and maybe, after all, the prince and herself were not so very happy when the cares of the world or old age came on them.'

Thus was the tale ended by poor old *Shebale* (Sybilla), Father Murphy's housekeeper, in Coolbawn, Barony of Bantry, about half a century since.

THE HAUGHTY PRINCESS[1]

Patrick Kennedy

There was once a very worthy king, whose daughter was the greatest beauty that could be seen far or near, but she was as proud as Lucifer, and no king or prince would she agree to marry. Her father was tired out at last, and invited every king, and prince, and duke, and earl that he knew or didn't know to come to his court to give her one trial more. They all came, and next day after breakfast they stood in a row in the lawn, and the princess walked along in the front of them to make her choice. One was fat, and says she, 'I won't have you, Beer-barrel!' One was tall and thin, and to him she said, 'I won't have you. Ramrod!' To a white-faced man she said, 'I won't have you, Pale Death'; and to a red-cheeked man she said, 'I won't have you, Cockscomb!' She stopped a little before the last of all, for he was a fine man in face and form. She wanted to find some defect in him, but he had nothing remarkable but a ring of brown curling hair under his chin. She admired him a little, and then carried it off with, 'I won't have you, Whiskers!'

So all went away, and the king was so vexed, he said to her, 'Now to punish your *impedence*, I'll give you to the first beggarman or singing *sthronshuch* that calls'; and, as sure as the hearth-money, a fellow all over rags, and hair that came to his shoulders, and a bushy red beard all over his face, came next morning, and began to sing before the parlour window.

When the song was over, the hall-door was opened, the singer asked in, the priest brought, and the princess married to Beardy. She roared and she bawled, but her father didn't mind her. 'There,' says he to the

---

1 *Fireside Stories of Ireland.*

THE HAUGHTY PRINCESS

bridegroom, 'is five guineas for you. Take your wife out of my sight, and never let me lay eyes on you or her again.'

Off he led her, and dismal enough she was. The only thing that gave her relief was the tones of her husband's voice and his genteel manners. 'Whose wood is this?' said she, as they were going through one. 'It belongs to the king you called Whiskers yesterday.' He gave her the same answer about meadows and corn-fields, and at last a fine city. 'Ah, what a fool I was!' said she to herself. 'He was a fine man, and I might have him for a husband.' At last they were coming up to a poor cabin. 'Why are you bringing me here?' says the poor lady. 'This was my house,' said he, 'and now it's yours.' She began to cry, but she was tired and hungry, and she went in with him.

Ovoch! there was neither a table laid out, nor a fire burning, and she was obliged to help her husband to light it, and boil their dinner, and clean up the place after; and next day he made her put on a stuff gown and a cotton handkerchief. When she had her house readied up, and no business to keep her employed, he brought home *sallies* [willows], peeled them, and showed her how to make baskets. But the hard twigs bruised her delicate fingers, and she began to cry. Well, then he asked her to mend their clothes, but the needle drew blood from her fingers, and she cried again. He couldn't bear to see her tears, so he bought a creel of earthenware, and sent her to the market to sell them. This was the hardest trial of all, but she looked so handsome and sorrowful, and had such a nice air about her, that all her pans, and jugs, and plates, and dishes were gone before noon, and the only mark of her old pride she showed was a slap she gave a buckeen across the face when he *axed* her to go in an' take share of a quart.

Well, her husband was so glad, he sent her with another creel the next day; but faith! her luck was after deserting her. A drunken huntsman came up riding, and his beast got in among her ware, and made *brishe* of every mother's son of 'em. She went home cryin', and her husband wasn't at all pleased. 'I see,' said he, 'you're not fit for business. Come along, I'll get you a kitchen-maid's place in the palace. I know the cook.'

So the poor thing was obliged to stifle her pride once more. She was

THE MAGICAL FOLK OF IRELAND

kept very busy, and the footman and the butler would be very impudent about looking for a kiss, but she let a screech out of her the first attempt was made, and the cook gave the fellow such a lambasting with the besom that he made no second offer. She went home to her husband every night, and she carried broken victuals wrapped in papers in her side pockets.

A week after she got service there was great bustle in the kitchen. The king was going to be married, but no one knew who the bride was to be. Well, in the evening the cook filled the princess's pockets with cold meat and puddings, and, says she, 'Before you go, let us have a look at the great doings in the big parlour.' So they came near the door to get a peep, and who should come out but the king himself, as handsome as you please, and no other but King Whiskers himself. 'Your handsome helper must pay for her peeping,' said he to the cook, 'and dance a jig with me.' Whether she would or no, he held her hand and brought her into the parlour. The fiddlers struck up, and away went *him* with *her*. But they hadn't danced two steps when the meat and the *puddens* flew out of her pockets. Every one roared out, and she flew to the door, crying piteously. But she was soon caught by the king, and taken into the back parlour. 'Don't you know me, my darling?' said he. 'I'm both King Whiskers, your husband the ballad-singer, and the drunken huntsman. Your father knew me well enough when he gave you to me, and all was to drive your pride out of you.' Well, she didn't know how she was with fright, and shame, and joy. Love was uppermost anyhow, for she laid her head on her husband's breast and cried like a child. The maids-of-honour soon had her away and dressed her as fine as hands and pins could do it; and there were her mother and father, too; and while the company were wondering what end of the handsome girl and the king, he and his queen, who they didn't know in her fine clothes, and the other king and queen, came in, and such rejoicings and fine doings as there was, none of us will ever see, any way.

THE ENCHANTMENT OF GEAROIDH IARLA

By Patrick Kennedy[1]

In old times in Ireland there was a great man of the Fitzgeralds. The name on him was Gerald, but the Irish, that always had a great liking for the family, called him *Gearoidh Iarla* (Earl Gerald). He had a great castle or rath at *Mullymast* (Mullaghmast); and whenever the English Government were striving to put some wrong on the country, he was always the man that stood up for it. Along with being a great leader in a fight, and very skilful at all weapons, he was deep in the *black art*, and could change himself into whatever shape he pleased. His lady knew that he had this power, and often asked him to let her into some of his secrets, but he never would gratify her.

She wanted particularly to see him in some strange shape, but he put her off and off on one pretence or other. But she wouldn't be a woman if she hadn't perseverance; and so at last he let her know that if she took the least fright while he'd be out of his natural form, he would never recover it till many generations of men would be under the mould. 'Oh! she wouldn't be a fit wife for Gearoidh Iarla if she could be easily frightened. Let him but gratify her in this whim, and he'd see what a hero she was!' So one beautiful summer evening, as they were sitting in their grand drawing-room, he turned his face away from her and muttered some words, and while you'd wink he was clever and clean out of sight, and a lovely *goldfinch* was flying about the room.

The lady, as courageous as she thought herself, was a little startled, but she held her own pretty well, especially when he came and perched

1 *Legendary Fiction of the Irish Celts* (Macmillan).

THE MAGICAL FOLK OF IRELAND

on her shoulder, and shook his wings, and put his little beak to her lips, and whistled the delightfulest tune you ever heard. Well, he flew in circles round the room, and played *hide and go seek* with his lady, and flew out into the garden, and flew back again, and lay down in her lap as if he was asleep, and jumped up again.

Well, when the thing had lasted long enough to satisfy both, he took one flight more into the open air; but by my word he was soon on his return. He flew right into his lady's bosom, and the next moment a fierce hawk was after him. The wife gave one loud scream, though there was no need, for the wild bird came in like an arrow, and struck against a table with such force that the life was dashed out of him. She turned her eyes from his quivering body to where she saw the goldfinch an instant before, but neither goldfinch nor Earl Gerald did she ever lay eyes on again.

Once every seven years the Earl rides round the Curragh of Kildare on a steed, whose silver shoes were half an inch thick the time he disappeared; and when these shoes are worn as thin as a cat's ear, he will be restored to the society of living men, fight a great battle with the English, and reign king of Ireland for two-score years.[2]

Himself and his warriors are now sleeping in a long cavern under the Rath of Mullaghmast. There is a table running along through the middle of the cave. The Earl is sitting at the head, and his troopers down along in complete armour both sides of the table, and their heads resting on it. Their horses, saddled and bridled, are standing behind their masters in their stalls at each side; and when the day comes, the miller's son that's to be born with six fingers on each hand, will blow his trumpet, and the horses will stamp and whinny, and the knights awake and mount their steeds, and go forth to battle.

Some night that happens once in every seven years, while the Earl is riding round the Curragh, the entrance may be seen by any one chancing to pass by. About a hundred years ago, a horse-dealer that

---

2 The last time *Gearoidh Iarla* appeared the horse-shoes were as thin as a sixpence.

THE ENCHANTMENT OF GEAROIDH IARLA

was late abroad and a little drunk, saw the lighted cavern, and went in. The lights, and the stillness, and the sight of the men in armour, cowed him a good deal, and he became sober. His hands began to tremble, and he let a bridle fall on the pavement. The sound of the bit echoed through the long cave, and one of the warriors that was next him lifted his head a little, and said, in a deep hoarse voice, 'Is it time yet?' He had the wit to say, 'Not yet, but soon will', and the heavy helmet sunk down on the table. The horse-dealer made the best of his way out, and I never heard of any other one having got the same opportunity.

MUNACHAR AND MANACHAR

Translated literally from the Irish by Douglas Hyde

There once lived a Munachar and a Manachar, a long time ago, and it is a long time since it was, and if they were alive then they would not be alive now. They went out together to pick raspberries, and as many as Munachar used to pick Manachar used to eat. Munachar said he must go look for a rod to make a gad (a withy band) to hang Manachar, who ate his raspberries every one; and he came to the rod. 'God save you,' said the rod. 'God and Mary save you.' 'How far are you going?' 'Going looking for a rod, a rod to make a gad, a gad to hang Manachar, who ate my raspberries every one.'

'You will not get me,' said the rod, 'until you get an axe to cut me.' He came to the axe. 'God save you,' said the axe. 'God and Mary save you.' 'How far are you going?' 'Going looking for an axe, an axe to cut a rod, a rod to make a gad, a gad to hang Manachar, who ate my raspberries every one.'

'You will not get me,' said the axe, 'until you get a flag to edge me.' He came to the flag. 'God save you,' says the flag. 'God and Mary save you.' 'How far are you going?' 'Going looking for a flag to edge an axe, an axe to cut a rod, a rod to make a gad, a gad to hang Manachar, who ate my raspberries every one.'

'You will not get me,' says the flag, 'till you get water to wet me.' He came to the water. 'God save you,' says the water. 'God and Mary save you.' 'How far are you going?' 'Going looking for water, water to wet a flag to edge an axe, an axe to cut a rod, a rod to make a gad, a gad to hang Manachar, who ate my raspberries every one.'

'You will not get me,' said the water, 'until you get a deer who will swim me.' He came to the deer. 'God save you,' says the deer. 'God and Mary save you.' 'How far are you going?' 'Going looking for a deer,

MUNACHAR AND MANACHAR

a deer to swim water, water to wet a flag, a flag to edge an axe, an axe to cut a rod, a rod to make a gad, a gad to hang Manachar, who ate my raspberries every one.'

'You will not get me,' said the deer, 'until you get a hound who will hunt me.' He came to the hound. 'God save you,' says the hound. 'God and Mary save you.' 'How far are you going?' 'Going looking for a hound, a hound to hunt a deer, a deer to swim water, water to wet a flag, a flag to edge an axe, an axe to cut a rod, a rod to make a gad, a gad to hang Manachar, who ate my raspberries every one.'

'You will not get me,' said the hound, 'until you get a bit of butter to put in my claw.' He came to the butter. 'God save you,' says the butter. 'God and Mary save you.' 'How far are you going?' 'Going looking for butter, butter to go in the claw of a hound, a hound to hunt a deer, a deer to swim water, water to wet a flag, a flag to edge an axe, an axe to cut a rod, a rod to make a gad, a gad to hang Manachar, who ate my raspberries every one.'

'You will not get me,' said the butter, 'until you get a cat who shall scrape me.' He came to the cat. 'God save you,' said the cat. 'God and Mary save you.' 'How far are you going?' 'Going looking for a cat, a cat to scrape butter, butter to go in the claw of a hound, a hound to hunt deer, a deer to swim water, water to wet a flag, a flag to edge an axe, an axe to cut a rod, a rod to make a gad, a gad to hang Manachar, who ate my raspberries every one.'

'You will not get me,' said the cat, 'until you will get milk which you will give me.' He came to the cow. 'God save you,' said the cow. 'God and Mary save you.' 'How far are you going?' 'Going looking for a cow, a cow to give me milk, milk I will give to the cat, cat to scrape butter, butter to go in the claw of a hound, a hound to hunt deer, a deer to swim water, water to wet a flag, a flag to edge an axe, an axe to cut a rod, a rod to make a gad, a gad to hang Manachar, who ate my raspberries every one.'

'You will not get any milk from me,' said the cow, 'until you bring me a whisp of straw from those threshers yonder.' He came to the threshers. 'God save you,' said the threshers. 'God and Mary save ye.' 'How far are you going?' 'Going looking for a whisp of straw from ye

THE MAGICAL FOLK OF IRELAND

to give to the cow, the cow to give me milk, milk I will give to the cat, cat to scrape butter, butter to go in the claw of a hound, the hound to hunt a deer, the deer to swim water, water to wet a flag, flag to edge an axe, axe to cut a rod, a rod to make a gad, a gad to hang Manachar, who ate my raspberries every one.'

'You will not get any whisp of straw from us,' said the threshers, 'until you bring us the makings of a cake from the miller over yonder.' He came to the miller. 'God save you.' 'God and Mary save you.' 'How far are you going?' 'Going looking for the makings of a cake, which I will give to the threshers, the threshers to give me a whisp of straw, the whisp of straw I will give to the cow, the cow to give me milk, milk I will give to the cat, the cat to scrape butter, butter to go in the claw of a hound, the hound to hunt a deer, the deer to swim water, water to wet a flag, the flag to edge an axe, an axe to cut a rod, a rod to make a gad, a gad to hang Manachar, who ate my raspberries every one.'

'You will not get any makings of a cake from me,' said the miller, 'till you bring me the full of that sieve of water from the river over there.'

He took the sieve in his hand and went over to the river, but as often as ever he would stoop and fill it with water, the moment he raised it the water would run out of it again, and sure, if he had been there from that day till this, he never could have filled it. A crow went flying by him, over his head. 'Daub! daub!' said the crow. 'My soul to God, then,' said Munachar, 'but it's the good advice you have', and he took the red clay and the daub that was by the brink, and he rubbed it to the bottom of the sieve, until all the holes were filled, and then the sieve held the water, and he brought the water to the miller, and the miller gave him the makings of a cake, and he gave the makings of the cake to the threshers, and the threshers gave him a whisp of straw, and he gave the whisp of straw to the cow, and the cow gave him milk, the milk he gave to the cat, the cat scraped the butter, the butter went into the claw of the hound, the hound hunted the deer, the deer swam the water, the water wet the flag, the flag sharpened the axe, the axe cut the rod, and the rod made a gad, and when he had it ready – I'll go bail that Manachar was far enough away from him.

MUNACHAR AND MANACHAR

There is some tale like this in almost every language. It resembles that given in that splendid work of industry and patriotism: Campbell's *Tales of the West Highlands*, under the name of *Moonachug and Meenachug*, 'The English House that Jack built,' says Campbell, 'has eleven steps, the Scotch Old Woman with the Silver Penny has twelve, the Novsk Cock and Hen A-nutting has twelve, ten of which are double. The German story in Grimm has five or six, all single ideas.' This, however, is longer than any of them. It sometimes varies a little in the telling, and the actors' names are sometimes *Suracha* and *Muracha*, and the crow is sometimes a gull, who, instead of *daub! daub!* says *cuir cré rua lesh!*

DONALD AND HIS NEIGHBOURS

From *Hibernian Tales*[1]

Hudden and Dudden and Donald O'Nery were near neighbours in the barony of Balinconlig, and ploughed with three bullocks; but the two former, envying the present prosperity of the latter, determined to kill his bullock, to prevent his farm being properly cultivated and laboured, that going back in the world he might be induced to sell his lands, which they meant to get possession of. Poor Donald finding his bullock killed, immediately skinned it, and throwing the skin over his shoulder, with the fleshy side out, set off to the next town with it, to dispose of it to the best of his advantage. Going along the road a magpie flew on the top of the hide, and began picking it, chattering all the time. The bird had been taught to speak, and imitate the human voice, and Donald, thinking he understood some words it was saying, put round his hand and caught hold of it. Having got possession of it, he put it under his great-coat, and so went on to town. Having sold the hide, he went into an inn to take a dram, and following the landlady into the cellar, he gave the bird a squeeze which made it chatter some broken accents that surprised her very much. 'What is that I hear?' said she to Donald. 'I think it is talk, and yet I do not understand.' 'Indeed,' said Donald, 'it is a bird I have that tells me everything, and I always carry it with me to know when there is any danger. Faith,' says he, 'it says you have far better liquor than you are giving me.' 'That is strange,' said she, going to another cask of better quality, and asking him if he would sell the bird. 'I will,' said Donald, 'if I get enough for it.' 'I will fill your hat with silver if you leave it with me.' Donald was glad to hear the news,

1 A chap-book mentioned by Thackeray in his *Irish Sketch Book*.

DONALD AND HIS NEIGHBOURS

and taking the silver, set off, rejoicing at his good luck. He had not been long at home until he met with Hudden and Dudden. 'Misters,' said he, 'you thought you had done me a bad turn, but you could not have done me a better; for look here, what I have got for the hide,' showing them a hatful of silver; 'you never saw such a demand for hides in your life as there is at present.' Hudden and Dudden that very night killed their bullocks, and set out the next morning to sell their hides. On coming to the place they went through all the merchants, but could only get a trifle for them; at last they had to take what they could get, and came home in a great rage, and vowing revenge on poor Donald. He had a pretty good guess how matters would turn out, and he being under the kitchen window, he was afraid they would rob him, or perhaps kill him when asleep, and on that account when he was going to bed he left his old mother in his place, and lay down in her bed, which was in the other side of the house, and they taking the old woman for Donald, choked her in her bed, but he making some noise, they had to retreat, and leave the money behind them, which grieved them very much. However, by daybreak, Donald got his mother on his back, and carried her to town. Stopping at a well, he fixed his mother with her staff, as if she was stooping for a drink, and then went into a public-house convenient and called for a dram. 'I wish,' said he to a woman that stood near him, 'you would tell my mother to come in; she is at yon well trying to get a drink, and she is hard of hearing; if she does not observe you, give her a little shake and tell her that I want her.' The woman called her several times, but she seemed to take no notice; at length she went to her and shook her by the arm, but when she let her go again, she tumbled on her head into the well, and, as the woman thought, was drowned. She, in her great surprise and fear at the accident, told Donald what had happened. 'O mercy,' said he, 'what is this?' He ran and pulled her out of the well, weeping and lamenting all the time, and acting in such a manner that you would imagine that he had lost his senses. The woman, on the other hand, was far worse than Donald, for his grief was only feigned, but she imagined herself to be the cause of the old woman's death. The inhabitants of the town hearing what had happened, agreed to make Donald up a good sum of

THE MAGICAL FOLK OF IRELAND

money for his loss, as the accident happened in their place, and Donald brought a greater sum home with him than he got for the magpie. They buried Donald's mother, and as soon as he saw Hudden he showed them the last purse of money he had got. 'You thought to kill me last night,' said he, 'but it was good for me it happened on my mother, for I got all that purse for her to make gunpowder.'

That very night Hudden and Dudden killed their mothers, and the next morning set off with them to town. On coming to the town with their burthen on their backs, they went up and down crying, 'Who will buy old wives for gunpowder', so that everyone laughed at them, and the boys at last clotted them out of the place. They then saw the cheat, and vowed revenge on Donald, buried the old women, and set off in pursuit of him. Coming to his house, they found him sitting at his breakfast, and seizing him, put him in a sack, and went to drown him in a river at some distance. As they were going along the highway they raised a hare, which they saw had but three feet, and throwing off the sack, ran after her, thinking by her appearance she would be easily taken. In their absence there came a drover that way, and hearing Donald singing in the sack, wondered greatly what could be the matter. 'What is the reason,' said he, 'that you are singing, and you confined?' 'O, I am going to heaven,' said Donald, 'and in a short time I expect to be free from trouble.' 'O dear,' said the drover, 'what will I give you if you let me to your place?' 'Indeed, I do not know,' said he, 'it would take a good sum.' 'I have not much money,' said the drover, 'but I have twenty head of fine cattle, which I will give you to exchange places with me.' 'Well,' says Donald, 'I do not care if I should loose the sack, and I will come out.' In a moment the drover liberated him, and went into the sack himself, and Donald drove home the fine heifers, and left them in his pasture.

Hudden and Dudden having caught the hare, returned, and getting the sack on one of their backs, carried Donald, as they thought, to the river and threw him in, where he immediately sank. They then marched home, intending to take immediate possession of Donald's property, but how great was their surprise when they found him safe at home before them, with such a fine herd of cattle, whereas they knew he had

DONALD AND HIS NEIGHBOURS

none before. 'Donald,' said they, 'what is all this? We thought you were drowned, and yet you are here before us.' 'Ah!' said he, 'if I had but help along with me when you threw me in, it would have been the best job ever I met with, for of all the sight of cattle and gold that ever was seen is there, and no one to own them, but I was not able to manage more than what you see, and I could show you the spot where you might get hundreds.' They both swore they would be his friend, and Donald accordingly led them to a very deep part of the river, and lifted up a stone. 'Now,' said he, 'watch this', throwing it into the stream; 'there is the very place, and go in, one of you first, and if you want help, you have nothing to do but call.' Hudden jumping in, and sinking to the bottom, rose up again, and making a bubbling noise, as those do that are drowning, attempted to speak, but could not. 'What is that he is saying now?' says Dudden. 'Faith,' says Donald, 'he is calling for help; don't you hear him? Stand about,' said he, running back, 'till I leap in. I know how to do it better than any of you.' Dudden, to have the advantage of him, jumped in off the bank, and was drowned along with Hudden, and this was the end of Hudden and Dudden.

THE JACKDAW

Tom Moor was a linen draper in Sackville Street. His father, when he died, left him an affluent fortune, and a shop of excellent trade.

As he was standing at his door one day a countryman came up to him with a nest of jackdaws, and accosting him, says, 'Master, will you buy a nest of daws?' 'No, I don't want any.' 'Master,' replied the man, 'I will sell them all cheap; you shall have the whole nest for ninepence.' 'I don't want them,' answered Tom Moor, 'so go about your business.'

As the man was walking away one of the daws popped out his head, and cried 'Mawk, mawk.' 'Damn it,' says Tom Moor, 'that bird knows my name; halloo, country-man, what will you take for the bird?' 'Why, you shall have him for threepence.' Tom Moor bought him, had a cage made, and hung him up in the shop.

The journeymen took much notice of the bird, and would frequently tap at the bottom of the cage, and say, 'Who are you? Who are you? Tom Moor of Sackville Street.'

In a short time the jackdaw learned these words, and if he wanted victuals or water, would strike his bill against the cage, turn up the white of his eyes, cock his head, and cry, 'Who are you? who are you? Tom Moor of Sackville Street.'

Tom Moor was fond of gaming, and often lost large sums of money; finding his business neglected in his absence, he had a small hazard table set up in one corner of his dining-room, and invited a party of his friends to play at it.

The jackdaw had by this time become familiar; his cage was left open, and he hopped into every part of the house; sometimes he got into the dining-room, where the gentlemen were at play, and one of them being a constant winner, the others would say, 'Damn it, how he nicks them.' The bird learned these words also, and adding them

THE JACKDAW

to the former, would call, 'Who are you? who are you? Tom Moor of Sackville Street. Damn it, how he nicks them.'

Tom Moor, from repeated losses and neglect of business, failed in trade, and became a prisoner in the Fleet; he took his bird with him, and lived on the master's side, supported by friends, in a decent manner. They would sometimes ask what brought you here? when he used to lift up his hands and answer, 'Bad company, by G—.' The bird learned this likewise, and at the end of the former words, would say, 'What brought you here? Bad company, by G—.'

Some of Tom Moor's friends died, others went abroad, and by degrees he was totally deserted, and removed to the common side of the prison, where the jail distemper soon attacked him; and in the last stage of life, lying on a straw bed; the poor bird had been for two days without food or water, came to his feet, and striking his bill on the floor, calls out, 'Who are you? Tom Moor of Sackville Street; damn it, how he nicks them, damn it, how he nicks them. What brought you here? bad company, by G— , bad company, by G—.'

Tom Moor, who had attended to the bird, was struck with his words, and reflecting on himself, cried out, 'Good God, to what a situation am I reduced! my father, when he died, left me a good fortune and an established trade. I have spent my fortune, ruined my business, and am now dying in a loathsome jail; and to complete all, keeping that poor thing confined without support. I will endeavour to do one piece of justice before I die, by setting him at liberty.'

He made a struggle to crawl from his straw bed, opened the casement, and out flew the bird. A flight of jackdaws from the Temple were going over the jail, and Tom Moor's bird mixed among them. The gardener was then laying the plats of the Temple gardens, and as often as he placed them in the day the jackdaws pulled them up by night. They got a gun and attempted to shoot some of them; but, being cunning birds, they always placed one as a watch in the stump of a hollow tree; who, as soon as the gun was levelled cried 'Mawk', and away they flew.

The gardeners were advised to get a net, and the first night it was spread they caught fifteen; Tom Moor's bird was amongst them. One

THE MAGICAL FOLK OF IRELAND

of the men took the net into a garret of an uninhabited house, fastened the doors and windows, and turned the birds loose. 'Now,' said he, 'you black rascals, I will be revenged of you.' Taking hold of the first at hand, he twists her neck, and throwing him down, cries, 'There goes one.' Tom Moor's bird, who had hopped up to a beam at one corner of the room unobserved, as the man lays hold of the second, calls out, 'Damn it, how he nicks them.' The man alarmed, cries, 'Sure I heard a voice, but the house is uninhabited, and the door is fast; it could only be imagination.' On laying hold of the third, and twisting his neck, Tom's bird again says, 'Damn it, how he nicks them.' The man dropped the bird in his hand, and turning to where the voice came from, seeing the other with his mouth open, cries out, 'Who are you?' to which the bird answered, 'Tom Moor of Sackville Street, Tom Moor of Sackville Street.' 'The devil you are; and what brought you here.' Tom Moor's bird, lifting up his pinions, answered, 'Bad company, by G—, bad company, by G—.' The fellow, frightened almost out of his wits, opened the door, ran down stairs, and out of the house, followed by all the birds, who by this means regained their liberty.

THE STORY OF CONN-EDA; OR, THE GOLDEN APPLES OF LOUGH ERNE[1]

Translated from the original Irish of the Story-teller, Abraham McCoy, by Nicholas O'Kearney

It was long before the time the western districts of *Innis Fodhla*[2] had any settled name, but were indiscriminately called after the person who took possession of them, and whose name they retained only as long as his sway lasted, that a powerful king reigned over this part of the sacred island. He was a puissant warrior, and no individual was found able to compete with him either on land or sea, or question his right to his conquest. The great king of the west held uncontrolled sway from the island of Rathlin to the mouth of the Shannon by sea, and far as the glittering length by land. The ancient king of the west, whose name was Conn, was good as well as great, and passionately loved by his people. His queen was a *Breaton* (British) princess, and was equally beloved and esteemed, because she was the great counterpart of the king in every respect; for whatever good qualification was wanting in the one, the other was certain to indemnify the omission. It was plainly manifest that heaven approved of the career in life of the virtuous couple; for during their reign the earth produced exuberant crops, the trees fruited ninefold commensurate with their usual bearing, the

---

1 Printed first in the *Cambrian Journal*, 1855; reprinted and re-edited in the *Folk-Lore Record*, vol. ii.

2 *Innis Fodhla* – Island of Destiny, an old name for Ireland.

THE MAGICAL FOLK OF IRELAND

rivers, lakes and surrounding sea teemed with abundance of choice fish, while herds and flocks were unusually prolific, and kine and sheep yielded such abundance of rich milk that they shed it in torrents upon the pastures; and furrows and cavities were always filled with the pure lacteal produce of the dairy. All these were blessings heaped by heaven upon the western districts of *Innis Fodhla*, over which the benignant and just Conn swayed his sceptre, in approbation of the course of goverment he had marked out for his own guidance. It is needless to state that the people who owned the authority of this great and good sovereign were the happiest on the face of the wide expanse of earth. It was during his reign, and that of his son and successor, that Ireland acquired the title of the 'happy isle of the west' among foreign nations. Con Mór and his good Queen Eda reigned in great glory during many years; they were blessed with an only son, whom they named Conn-eda, after both his parents, because the Druids foretold at his birth that he would inherit the good qualities of both. According as the young prince grew in years, his amiable and benignant qualities of mind, as well as his great strength of body and manly bearing, became more manifest. He was the idol of his parents, and the boast of his people; he was beloved and respected to that degree that neither prince, lord, nor plebeian swore an oath by the sun, moon, stars, or elements, except by the head of Conn-eda. This career of glory, however, was doomed to meet a powerful but temporary impediment, for the good Queen Eda took a sudden and severe illness, of which she died in a few days, thus plunging her spouse, her son and all her people into a depth of grief and sorrow from which it was found difficult to relieve them.

The good king and his subjects mourned the loss of Queen Eda for a year and a day, and at the expiration of that time Conn Mor reluctantly yielded to the advice of his Druids and counsellors, and took to wife the daughter of his Arch-Druid. The new queen appeared to walk in the footsteps of the good Eda for several years, and gave great satisfaction to her subjects. But, in course of time, having had several children, and perceiving that Conn-eda was the favourite son of the king and the darling of the people, she clearly foresaw that he would become successor to the throne after the demise of his father, and that her son

THE STORY OF CONN-EDA

would certainly be excluded. This excited the hatred and inflamed the jealousy of the Druid's daughter against her step-son to such an extent, that she resolved in her own mind to leave nothing in her power undone to secure his death, or even exile from the kingdom. She began by circulating evil reports of the prince; but, as he was above suspicion, the king only laughed at the weakness of the queen; and the great princes and chieftains, supported by the people in general, gave an unqualified contradiction; while the prince himself bore all his trials with the utmost patience, and always repaid her bad and malicious acts towards him with good and benevolent ones. The enmity of the queen towards Conn-eda knew no bounds when she saw that the false reports she circulated could not injure him. As a last resource, to carry out her wicked projects, she determined to consult her *Cailleach-chearc* (hen-wife), who was a reputed enchantress.

Pursuant to her resolution, by the early dawn of morning she hied to the cabin of the *Cailleach-chearc*, and divulged to her the cause of her trouble. 'I cannot render you any help,' said the *Cailleach*, 'until you name the *duais*' (reward). 'What *duais* do you require?' asked the queen, impatiently. 'My *duais*,' replied the enchantress, 'is to fill the cavity of my arm with wool, and the hole I shall bore with my distaff with red wheat.' 'Your *duais* is granted, and shall be immediately given you,' said the queen. The enchantress thereupon stood in the door of her hut, and bending her arm into a circle with her side, directed the royal attendants to thrust the wool into her house through her arm, and she never permitted them to cease until all the available space within was filled with wool. She then got on the roof of her brother's house, and, having made a hole through it with her distaff, caused red wheat to be spilled through it, until that was filled up to the roof with red wheat, so that there was no room for another grain within. 'Now,' said the queen, 'since you have received your *duais*, tell me how I can accomplish my purpose.' 'Take this chess-board and chess, and invite the prince to play with you; you shall win the first game. The condition you shall make is, that whoever wins a game shall be at liberty to impose whatever *geasa* (conditions) the winner pleases on the loser. When you win, you must bid the prince, under the penalty

THE MAGICAL FOLK OF IRELAND

either to go into *ionarbadh* (exile), or procure for you, within the space of a year and a day, the three golden apples that grew in the garden, the *each dubh* (black steed), and *coileen con na mbuadh* (hound of supernatural powers), called Samer, which are in the possession of the king of the Firbolg race, who resides in Lough Erne.[3] Those two things are so precious, and so well guarded, that he can never attain them by his own power; and, if he would rashly attempt to seek them, he should lose his life.'

The queen was greatly pleased at the advice, and lost no time in inviting Conn-eda to play a game at chess, under the conditions she had been instructed to arrange by the enchantress. The queen won the game, as the enchantress foretold, but so great was her anxiety to have the prince completely in her power, that she was tempted to challenge him to play a second game, which Conn-eda, to her astonishment, and no less mortification, easily won. 'Now,' said the prince, 'since you won the first game, it is your duty to impose your *geis* first.' 'My *geis*,' said the queen, 'which I impose upon you, is to procure me the three golden apples that grow in the garden, the *each dubh* (black steed), and *cuileen con na mbuadh* (hound of supernatural powers), which are in the keeping of the king of the Firbolgs, in Lough Erne, within the space of a year and a day; or, in case you fail, to go into *ionarbadh* (exile), and never return, except you surrender yourself to lose your head and *comhead beatha* (preservation of life). 'Well, then,' said the prince, 'the *geis* which I bind you by, is to sit upon the pinnacle of yonder tower until my return, and to take neither food nor nourishment of any description, except what red-wheat you can pick up with the point of your bodkin; but if I do not return, you are at perfect liberty to come down at the expiration of the year and a day.'

In consequence of the severe *geis* imposed upon him, Conn-eda was very much troubled in mind; and, well knowing he had a long journey to make before he would reach his destination, immediately prepared

---

3 The Firbolgs believed their elysium to be under water. The peasantry still believe many lakes to be peopled. – See section on *T'yeer na n-Oge*.

THE STORY OF CONN-EDA

to set out on his way, not, however, before he had the satisfaction of witnessing the ascent of the queen to the place where she was obliged to remain exposed to the scorching sun of the summer and the blasting storms of winter, for the space of one year and a day, at least. Conn-eda being ignorant of what steps he should take to procure the *each dubh* and *cuileen con na mbuadh*, though he was well aware that human energy would prove unavailing, thought proper to consult the great Druid, Fionn Dadhna, of Sleabh Badhna, who was a friend of his before he ventured to proceed to Lough Erne. When he arrived at the bruighean of the Druid, he was received with cordial friendship, and the *failte* (welcome), as usual, was poured out before him, and when he was seated, warm water was fetched, and his feet bathed, so that the fatigue he felt after his journey was greatly relieved. The Druid, after he had partaken of refreshments, consisting of the newest of food and oldest of liquors, asked him the reason for paying the visit, and more particularly the cause of his sorrow; for the prince appeared exceedingly depressed in spirit. Conn-eda told his friend the whole history of the transaction with his stepmother from the beginning to end. 'Can you not assist me?' asked the Prince, with downcast countenance. 'I cannot, indeed, assist you at present,' replied the Druid; 'but I will retire to my *grianan* (green place) at sun-rising on the morrow, and learn by virtue of my Druidism what can be done to assist you.' The Druid, accordingly, as the sun rose on the following morning, retired to his *grianan*, and consulted the god he adored, through the power of his *draoidheacht*.[4] When he returned, he called Conn-eda aside on the plain, and addressed him thus: 'My dear son, I find you have been under a severe – an almost impossible – *geis* intended for your destruction; no person on earth could have advised the queen to impose it except the Cailleach of Lough Corrib, who is the greatest Druidess now in Ireland, and sister to the Firbolg, King of Lough Erne. It is not in my power, nor in that of the Deity I adore, to interfere in your behalf;

---

4 *Draoidheacht*, i.e., the Druidic worship; magic, sorcery, divination.

THE MAGICAL FOLK OF IRELAND

but go directly to Sliabh Mis, and consult *Eánchinn-duine* (the bird of the human head), and if there be any possibility of relieving you, that bird can do it, for there is not a bird in the western world so celebrated as that bird, because it knows all things that are past, all things that are present and exist, and all things that shall hereafter exist. It is difficult to find access to his place of concealment, and more difficult still to obtain an answer from him; but I will endeavour to regulate that matter for you; and that is all I can do for you at present.'

The Arch-Druid then instructed him thus: – 'Take,' said he, 'yonder little shaggy steed, and mount him immediately, for in three days the bird will make himself visible, and the little shaggy steed will conduct you to his place of abode. But lest the bird should refuse to reply to your queries, take this precious stone (*leag lorgmhar*), and present it to him, and then little danger and doubt exist but that he will give you a ready answer.' The prince returned heartfelt thanks to the Druid, and, having saddled and mounted the little shaggy horse without much delay, received the precious stone from the Druid, and, after having taken his leave of him, set out on his journey. He suffered the reins to fall loose upon the neck of the horse according as he had been instructed, so that the animal took whatever road he chose.

It would be tedious to relate the numerous adventures he had with the little shaggy horse, which had the extraordinary gift of speech, and was a *draoidheacht* horse during his journey.

The Prince having reached the hiding-place of the strange bird at the appointed time, and having presented him with the *leag lorgmhar*, according to Fionn Badhna's instructions, and proposed his questions relative to the manner he could best arrange for the fulfilment of his *geis*, the bird took up in his mouth the jewel from the stone on which it was placed, and flew to an inaccessible rock at some distance, and, when there perched, he thus addressed the prince, 'Conn-eda, son of the King of Cruachan,' said he, in a loud, croaking human voice, 'remove the stone just under your right foot, and take the ball of iron and *corna* (cup) you shall find under it; then mount your horse, cast the ball before you, and having so done, your horse will tell you all the other things necessary to be done.' The bird, having said this,

THE STORY OF CONN-EDA

immediately flew out of sight.

Conn-eda took great care to do everything according to the instructions of the bird. He found the iron ball and *corna* in the place which had been pointed out. He took them up, mounted his horse, and cast the ball before him. The ball rolled on at a regular gait, while the little shaggy horse followed on the way it led until they reached the margin of Lough Erne. Here the ball rolled in the water and became invisible. 'Alight now,' said the *draoidheacht* pony, 'and put your hand into mine ear; take from thence the small bottle of *íce* (all-heal) and the little wicker basket which you will find there, and remount with speed, for just now your great dangers and difficulties commence.' Conn-eda, ever faithful to the kind advice of his *draoidheacht* pony, did what he had been advised. Having taken the basket and bottle of *íce* from the animal's ear, he remounted and proceeded on his journey, while the water of the lake appeared only like an atmosphere above his head. When he entered the lake the ball again appeared, and rolled along until it came to the margin, across which was a causeway, guarded by three frightful serpents; the hissings of the monsters was heard at a great distance, while, on a nearer approach, their yawning mouths and formidable fangs were quite sufficient to terrify the stoutest heart. 'Now,' said the horse, 'open the basket and cast a piece of the meat you find in it into the mouth of each serpent; when you have done this, secure yourself in your seat in the best manner you can, so that we may make all due arrangements to pass those *draoidheacht peists*. If you cast the pieces of meat into the mouth of each peist unerringly, we shall pass them safely, otherwise we are lost.' Conn-eda flung the pieces of meat into the jaws of the serpents with unerring aim. 'Bare a benison and victory,' said the *draoidheacht* steed, 'for you are a youth that will win and prosper.' And, on saying these words, he sprang aloft, and cleared in his leap the river and ford, guarded by the serpents, seven measures beyond the margin. 'Are you still mounted, prince Conn-eda?' said the steed. 'It has taken only half my exertion to remain so,' replied Conn-eda. 'I find,' said the pony, 'that you are a young prince that deserves to succeed; one danger is now over, but two others remain.' They proceeded onwards after the ball until they

THE MAGICAL FOLK OF IRELAND

came in view of a great mountain flaming with fire. 'Hold yourself in readiness for another dangerous leap,' said the horse. The trembling prince had no answer to make, but seated himself as securely as the magnitude of the danger before him would permit. The horse in the next instant sprang from the earth, and flew like an arrow over the burning mountain. 'Are you still alive, Conn-eda, son of Conn-mór?' inquired the faithful horse. 'I'm just alive, and no more, for I'm greatly scorched,' answered the prince. 'Since you are yet alive, I feel assured that you are a young man destined to meet supernatural success and benisons,' said the Druidic steed. 'Our greatest dangers are over,' added he, 'and there is hope that we shall overcome the next and last danger.' After they had proceeded a short distance, his faithful steed, addressing Conn-eda, said, 'Alight, now, and apply a portion of the little bottle of *íce* to your wounds.' The prince immediately followed the advice of his monitor, and, as soon as he rubbed the *íce* (all-heal) to bis wounds, he became as whole and fresh as ever he had been before. After having done this, Conn-eda remounted, and following the track of the ball, soon came in sight of a great city surrounded by high walls. The only gate that was visible was not defended by armed men, but by two great towers that emitted flames that could be seen at a great distance. 'Alight on this plain,' said the steed, 'and take a small knife from my other ear; and with this knife you shall kill and flay me. When you have done this, envelop yourself in my hide, and you can pass the gate unscathed and unmolested. When you get inside you can come out at pleasure; because when once you enter there is no danger, and you can pass and repass whenever you wish; and let me tell you that all I have to ask of you in return is that you, when once inside the gates, will immediately return and drive away the birds of prey that may be fluttering round to feed on my carcass; and more, that you will pour any drop of that powerful *íce*, if such still remain in the bottle, upon my flesh, to preserve it from corruption. When you do this in memory of me, if it be not too troublesome, dig a pit, and cast my remains into it.'

'Well,' said Conn-eda, 'my noblest steed, because you have been so faithful to me hitherto, and because you still would have rendered me further service, I consider such a proposal insulting to my feelings as

THE STORY OF CONN-EDA

a man, and totally in variance with the spirit which can feel the value of gratitude, not to speak of my feelings as a prince. But as a prince I am able to say, Come what may – come death itself in its most hideous forms and terrors – I never will sacrifice private friendship to personal interest. Hence, I am, I swear by my arms of valour, prepared to meet the worst – even death itself – sooner than violate the principles of humanity, honour and friendship! What a sacrifice do you propose!' 'Pshaw, man! heed not that; do what I advise you, and prosper.' 'Never! never!' exclaimed the prince. 'Well, then, son of the great western monarch,' said the horse, with a tone of sorrow, 'if you do not follow my advice on this occasion, I tell you that both you and I shall perish, and shall never meet again; but, if you act as I have instructed you, matters shall assume a happier and more pleasing aspect than you may imagine. I have not misled you heretofore, and, if I have not, what need have you to doubt the most important portion of my counsel? Do exactly as I have directed you, else you will cause a worse fate than death to befall me. And, moreover, I can tell you that, if you persist in your resolution, I have done with you for ever.'

When the prince found that his noble steed could not be persuaded from his purpose, he took the knife out of his ear with reluctance, and with a faltering and trembling hand essayed experimentally to point the weapon at his throat. Conn-eda's eyes were bathed in tears; but no sooner had he pointed the Druidic *scian* to the throat of his good steed, than the dagger, as if impelled by some Druidic power, stuck in his neck, and in an instant the work of death was done, and the noble animal fell dead at his feet. When the prince saw his noble steed fall dead by his hand, he cast himself on the ground, and cried aloud until his consciousness was gone. When he recovered, he perceived that the steed was quite dead; and, as he thought there was no hope of resuscitating him, he considered it the most prudent course he could adopt to act according to the advice he had given him. After many misgivings of mind and abundant showers of tears, he essayed the task of flaying him, which was only that of a few minutes. When he found he had the hide separated from the body, he, in the derangement of the moment, enveloped himself in it, and proceeding towards the

THE MAGICAL FOLK OF IRELAND

magnificent city in rather a demented state of mind, entered it without any molestation or opposition. It was a surprisingly populous city, and an extremely wealthy place; but its beauty, magnificence, and wealth had no charms for Conn-eda, because the thoughts of the loss he sustained in his dear steed were paramount to those of all other earthly considerations.

He had scarcely proceeded more than fifty paces from the gate, when the last request of his beloved *draoidheacht* steed forced itself upon his mind, and compelled him to return to perform the last solemn injunctions upon him. When he came to the spot upon which the remains of his beloved *draoidheacht* steed lay, an appalling sight presented itself; ravens and other carnivorous birds of prey were tearing and devouring the flesh of his dear steed. It was but short work to put them to flight; and having uncorked his little jar of *íce*, he deemed it a labour of love to embalm the now mangled remains with the precious ointment. The potent *íce* had scarcely touched the inanimate flesh, when, to the surprise of Conn-eda, it commenced to undergo some strange change, and in a few minutes, to his unspeakable astonishment and joy, it assumed the form of one of the handsomest and noblest young men imaginable, and in the twinkling of an eye the prince was locked in his embrace, smothering him with kisses, and drowning him with tears of joy. When one recovered from his ecstasy of joy, the other from his surprise, the strange youth thus addressed the prince: 'Most noble and puissant prince, you are the best sight I ever saw with my eyes, and I am the most fortunate being in existence for having met you! Behold in my person, changed to the natural shape, your little shaggy *draoidheacht* steed! I am brother of the king of the city; and it was the wicked Druid, Fion Badhna, who kept me so long in bondage; but he was forced to give me up when you came to *consult* him, for my *geis* was then broken; yet I could not recover my pristine shape and appearance unless you had acted as you have kindly done. It was my own sister that urged the queen, your step-mother, to send you in quest of the steed and powerful puppy hound, which my brother has now in keeping. My sister, rest assured, had no thought of doing you the least injury, but much good, as you will find hereafter; because, if she were

THE STORY OF CONN-EDA

maliciously inclined towards you, she could have accomplished her end without any trouble. In short, she only wanted to free you from all future danger and disaster, and recover me from my relentless enemies through your instrumentality. Come with me, my friend and deliverer, and the steed and the puppy-hound of extraordinary powers, and the golden apples, shall be yours, and a cordial welcome shall greet you in my brother's abode; for you will deserve all this and much more.'

The exciting joy felt on the occasion was mutual, and they lost no time in idle congratulations, but proceeded on to the royal residence of the King of Lough Erne. Here they were both received with demonstrations of joy by the king and his chieftains; and, when the purpose of Conn-eda's visit became known to the king, he gave a free consent to bestow on Conn-eda the black steed, the *coileen con-na-mbuadh*, called Samer, and the three apples of health that were growing in his garden, under the special condition, however, that he would consent to remain as his guest until he could set out on his journey in proper time, to fulfil his *geis*. Conn-eda, at the earnest solicitation of his friends, consented, and remained in the royal residence of the Firbolg, King of Lough Erne, in the enjoyment of the most delicious and fascinating pleasures during that period.

When the time of his departure came, the three golden apples were plucked from the crystal tree in the midst of the pleasure-garden, and deposited in his bosom; the puppy-hound, Samer, was leashed, and the leash put into his hand; and the black steed, richly harnessed, was got in readiness for him to mount. The king himself helped him on horseback, and both he and his brother assured him that he might not fear burning mountains or hissing serpents, because none would impede him, as his steed was always a passport to and from his subaqueous kingdom. And both he and his brother extorted a promise from Conn-eda, that he would visit them once every year at least.

Conn-eda took leave of his dear friend, and the king his brother. The parting was a tender one, soured by regret on both sides. He proceeded on his way without meeting anything to obstruct him, and in due time came in sight of the *dún* of his father, where the queen had been placed on the pinnacle of the tower, in full hope that, as it was the last day of

THE MAGICAL FOLK OF IRELAND

her imprisonment there, the prince would not make his appearance, and thereby forfeit all pretensions and right to the crown of his father for ever. But her hopes were doomed to meet a disappointment, for when it had been announced to her by her couriers, who had been posted to watch the arrival of the prince, that he approached, she was incredulous; but when she saw him mounted on a foaming black steed, richly harnessed, and leading a strange kind of animal by a silver chain, she at once knew he was returning in triumph, and that her schemes laid for his destruction were frustrated. In the excess of grief at her disappointment, she cast herself from the top of the tower, and was instantly dashed to pieces. Conn-eda met a welcome reception from his father, who mourned him as lost to him for ever, during his absence; and, when the base conduct of the queen became known, the king and his chieftains ordered her remains to be consumed to ashes for her perfidy and wickedness.

Conn-eda planted the three golden apples in his garden, and instantly a great tree, bearing similar fruit, sprang up. This tree caused all the district to produce an exuberance of crops and fruits, so that it became as fertile and plentiful as the dominions of the Firbolgs, in consequence of the extraordinary powers possessed by the golden fruit. The hound Samer and the steed were of the utmost utility to him; and his reign was long and prosperous, and celebrated among the old people for the great abundance of corn, fruit, milk, fowl and fish that prevailed during this happy reign. It was after the name Conn-eda the province of Connaucht, or *Conneda*, or *Connacht*, was so called.